BREAST
CANCER
TRIALS

The Australian Women's Health Diary
funds breast cancer clinical trials research
to save and improve the lives of every
person affected by breast cancer.

Today, tomorrow and forever.

TRIALS SAVE LIVES

Thanks to you, this diary is saving lives

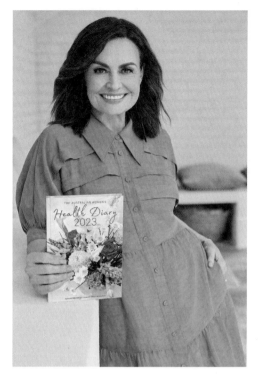

This special diary is celebrating a big birthday – 25 years!

If you're a long-term buyer or a new one – thank you. You've helped make possible the life-saving treatments available to people diagnosed with breast cancer today.

But sadly, the need for more research is still urgent and still unmet. Breast cancer still takes lives, ends dreams and reduces quality of life for too many people.

Only breast cancer clinical trials research can turn laboratory breakthroughs, which are happening at a rapid pace, into new treatments and cures for the 55 people diagnosed with breast cancer in Australia every day.

The researchers at Breast Cancer Trials, who conduct national and international breast cancer clinical trials, are committed to ending the pain and loss of breast cancer. I know, like me, you are too.

Through their research, we can make sure every patient will benefit from effective and personalised treatments that can save their lives, and that their survival does not come with a high cost of pain and lasting side effects.

I hope you're as proud as I am of this 25th edition and all that this diary has achieved so far. My sincere thanks to the women who feature this year. I hope as you use your diary, they'll remind you of the difference you're making in the lives of others.

May this year be a healthy and happy one for you!

Lisa x

LISA WILKINSON

BREAST
CANCER
TRIALS

Who we are

Breast Cancer Trials is a research charity, which conducts national and international clinical trials in breast cancer. Our researchers, located in hospitals throughout Australia and New Zealand, treat and support patients with breast cancer every day. They are uniquely placed to develop new breast cancer clinical trials which address critical areas of patient need.

Why we do clinical trials

Breast cancer is not one single disease. Every person requires a treatment plan personalised to their type of breast cancer and other individual factors such as the size, stage and location of the breast cancer and their age and menopausal status. Our aim is to get the best possible treatment to every individual person so they have the greatest chance of long-term cure.

People diagnosed with breast cancer today are benefitting from the treatments identified in past clinical trials that we have conducted. Similarly, the clinical trials we conduct today can give people access to potential new breast cancer treatments and prevention options. And what we learn from these trials will influence how breast cancer is treated and prevented for people in the future.

Our research focus

Our priority research areas include: stopping breast cancer from occurring in the first place; curing more people with targeted treatment at the time of their first diagnosis to prevent any chance of recurrence of their disease; helping patients with metastatic breast cancer to live longer with good quality of life; and protecting quality of life by reducing the side effects of treatment.

Your support

Our research is made possible thanks to the women and men who participate in our clinical trials and our generous supporters, like you, who donate and buy this diary. Thank you for working with us to save every life from breast cancer, to protect quality of life and to prevent breast cancer.

SCAN THIS QR CODE TO LEARN MORE.

Calendar
2023

JANUARY
S	M	T	W	T	F	S
1	2	3	4	5	6	7
8	9	10	11	12	13	14
15	16	17	18	19	20	21
22	23	24	25	26	27	28
29	30	31				

FEBRUARY
S	M	T	W	T	F	S
			1	2	3	4
5	6	7	8	9	10	11
12	13	14	15	16	17	18
19	20	21	22	23	24	25
26	27	28				

MARCH
S	M	T	W	T	F	S
			1	2	3	4
5	6	7	8	9	10	11
12	13	14	15	16	17	18
19	20	21	22	23	24	25
26	27	28	29	30	31	

APRIL
S	M	T	W	T	F	S
30						1
2	3	4	5	6	7	8
9	10	11	12	13	14	15
16	17	18	19	20	21	22
23	24	25	26	27	28	29

MAY
S	M	T	W	T	F	S
	1	2	3	4	5	6
7	8	9	10	11	12	13
14	15	16	17	18	19	20
21	22	23	24	25	26	27
28	29	30	31			

JUNE
S	M	T	W	T	F	S
				1	2	3
4	5	6	7	8	9	10
11	12	13	14	15	16	17
18	19	20	21	22	23	24
25	26	27	28	29	30	

JULY
S	M	T	W	T	F	S
30	31					1
2	3	4	5	6	7	8
9	10	11	12	13	14	15
16	17	18	19	20	21	22
23	24	25	26	27	28	29

AUGUST
S	M	T	W	T	F	S
		1	2	3	4	5
6	7	8	9	10	11	12
13	14	15	16	17	18	19
20	21	22	23	24	25	26
27	28	29	30	31		

SEPTEMBER
S	M	T	W	T	F	S
					1	2
3	4	5	6	7	8	9
10	11	12	13	14	15	16
17	18	19	20	21	22	23
24	25	26	27	28	29	30

OCTOBER
S	M	T	W	T	F	S
1	2	3	4	5	6	7
8	9	10	11	12	13	14
15	16	17	18	19	20	21
22	23	24	25	26	27	28
29	30	31				

NOVEMBER
S	M	T	W	T	F	S
			1	2	3	4
5	6	7	8	9	10	11
12	13	14	15	16	17	18
19	20	21	22	23	24	25
26	27	28	29	30		

DECEMBER
S	M	T	W	T	F	S
31					1	2
3	4	5	6	7	8	9
10	11	12	13	14	15	16
17	18	19	20	21	22	23
24	25	26	27	28	29	30

2022

JANUARY
S	M	T	W	T	F	S
30	31					1
2	3	4	5	6	7	8
9	10	11	12	13	14	15
16	17	18	19	20	21	22
23	24	25	26	27	28	29

FEBRUARY
S	M	T	W	T	F	S
		1	2	3	4	5
6	7	8	9	10	11	12
13	14	15	16	17	18	19
20	21	22	23	24	25	26
27	28					

MARCH
S	M	T	W	T	F	S
		1	2	3	4	5
6	7	8	9	10	11	12
13	14	15	16	17	18	19
20	21	22	23	24	25	26
27	28	29	30	31		

APRIL
S	M	T	W	T	F	S
					1	2
3	4	5	6	7	8	9
10	11	12	13	14	15	16
17	18	19	20	21	22	23
24	25	26	27	28	29	30

MAY
S	M	T	W	T	F	S
1	2	3	4	5	6	7
8	9	10	11	12	13	14
15	16	17	18	19	20	21
22	23	24	25	26	27	28
29	30	31				

JUNE
S	M	T	W	T	F	S
			1	2	3	4
5	6	7	8	9	10	11
12	13	14	15	16	17	18
19	20	21	22	23	24	25
26	27	28	29	30		

JULY
S	M	T	W	T	F	S
31					1	2
3	4	5	6	7	8	9
10	11	12	13	14	15	16
17	18	19	20	21	22	23
24	25	26	27	28	29	30

AUGUST
S	M	T	W	T	F	S
	1	2	3	4	5	6
7	8	9	10	11	12	13
14	15	16	17	18	19	20
21	22	23	24	25	26	27
28	29	30	31			

SEPTEMBER
S	M	T	W	T	F	S
				1	2	3
4	5	6	7	8	9	10
11	12	13	14	15	16	17
18	19	20	21	22	23	24
25	26	27	28	29	30	

OCTOBER
S	M	T	W	T	F	S
30	31					1
2	3	4	5	6	7	8
9	10	11	12	13	14	15
16	17	18	19	20	21	22
23	24	25	26	27	28	29

NOVEMBER
S	M	T	W	T	F	S
		1	2	3	4	5
6	7	8	9	10	11	12
13	14	15	16	17	18	19
20	21	22	23	24	25	26
27	28	29	30			

DECEMBER
S	M	T	W	T	F	S
				1	2	3
4	5	6	7	8	9	10
11	12	13	14	15	16	17
18	19	20	21	22	23	24
25	26	27	28	29	30	31

2024

JANUARY
S	M	T	W	T	F	S
	1	2	3	4	5	6
7	8	9	10	11	12	13
14	15	16	17	18	19	20
21	22	23	24	25	26	27
28	29	30	31			

FEBRUARY
S	M	T	W	T	F	S
				1	2	3
4	5	6	7	8	9	10
11	12	13	14	15	16	17
18	19	20	21	22	23	24
25	26	27	28	29		

MARCH
S	M	T	W	T	F	S
31					1	2
3	4	5	6	7	8	9
10	11	12	13	14	15	16
17	18	19	20	21	22	23
24	25	26	27	28	29	30

APRIL
S	M	T	W	T	F	S
	1	2	3	4	5	6
7	8	9	10	11	12	13
14	15	16	17	18	19	20
21	22	23	24	25	26	27
28	29	30				

MAY
S	M	T	W	T	F	S
			1	2	3	4
5	6	7	8	9	10	11
12	13	14	15	16	17	18
19	20	21	22	23	24	25
26	27	28	29	30	31	

JUNE
S	M	T	W	T	F	S
30						1
2	3	4	5	6	7	8
9	10	11	12	13	14	15
16	17	18	19	20	21	22
23	24	25	26	27	28	29

JULY
S	M	T	W	T	F	S
	1	2	3	4	5	6
7	8	9	10	11	12	13
14	15	16	17	18	19	20
21	22	23	24	25	26	27
28	29	30	31			

AUGUST
S	M	T	W	T	F	S
				1	2	3
4	5	6	7	8	9	10
11	12	13	14	15	16	17
18	19	20	21	22	23	24
25	26	27	28	29	30	31

SEPTEMBER
S	M	T	W	T	F	S
1	2	3	4	5	6	7
8	9	10	11	12	13	14
15	16	17	18	19	20	21
22	23	24	25	26	27	28
29	30					

OCTOBER
S	M	T	W	T	F	S
		1	2	3	4	5
6	7	8	9	10	11	12
13	14	15	16	17	18	19
20	21	22	23	24	25	26
27	28	29	30	31		

NOVEMBER
S	M	T	W	T	F	S
					1	2
3	4	5	6	7	8	9
10	11	12	13	14	15	16
17	18	19	20	21	22	23
24	25	26	27	28	29	30

DECEMBER
S	M	T	W	T	F	S
1	2	3	4	5	6	7
8	9	10	11	12	13	14
15	16	17	18	19	20	21
22	23	24	25	26	27	28
29	30	31				

Personal information

IF FOUND PLEASE CONTACT:

NAME

ADDRESS

STATE   POSTCODE

PHONE NUMBER   MOBILE

EMAIL

IN CASE OF EMERGENCY:

NAME

TELEPHONE   MOBILE

USEFUL TELEPHONE NUMBERS:

DOCTOR   GAS

DENTIST   ELECTRICITY

MECHANIC   WATER

VET   PLUMBER

CHILD CARE   SCHOOL

OTHER IMPORTANT INFORMATION:

Key contacts

NAME

ADDRESS

	STATE	POSTCODE

TELEPHONE (H) (W)

MOBILE EMAIL

NAME

ADDRESS

	STATE	POSTCODE

TELEPHONE (H) (W)

MOBILE EMAIL

NAME

ADDRESS

	STATE	POSTCODE

TELEPHONE (H) (W)

MOBILE EMAIL

NAME

ADDRESS

	STATE	POSTCODE

TELEPHONE (H) (W)

MOBILE EMAIL

NAME

ADDRESS

	STATE	POSTCODE

TELEPHONE (H) (W)

MOBILE EMAIL

NAME

ADDRESS

	STATE	POSTCODE

TELEPHONE (H) (W)

MOBILE EMAIL

Key contacts

NAME

ADDRESS

STATE   POSTCODE

TELEPHONE (H)   (W)

MOBILE   EMAIL

NAME

ADDRESS

STATE   POSTCODE

TELEPHONE (H)   (W)

MOBILE   EMAIL

NAME

ADDRESS

STATE   POSTCODE

TELEPHONE (H)   (W)

MOBILE   EMAIL

NAME

ADDRESS

STATE   POSTCODE

TELEPHONE (H)   (W)

MOBILE   EMAIL

NAME

ADDRESS

STATE   POSTCODE

TELEPHONE (H)   (W)

MOBILE   EMAIL

NAME

ADDRESS

STATE   POSTCODE

TELEPHONE (H)   (W)

MOBILE   EMAIL

Special events 2023

JANUARY

FEBRUARY

MARCH

APRIL

MAY

JUNE

JULY

AUGUST

SEPTEMBER

OCTOBER

NOVEMBER

DECEMBER

School terms 2023

NEW SOUTH WALES

TERM 1	January 27 – April 6
TERM 2	April 24 – June 30
TERM 3	July 17 – September 22
TERM 4	October 9 – December 19

AUSTRALIAN CAPITAL TERRITORY

TERM 1	January 27 – April 6
TERM 2	April 24 – June 30
TERM 3	July 17 – September 22
TERM 4	October 9 – December 15

QUEENSLAND

TERM 1	January 23 – March 31
TERM 2	April 17 – June 23
TERM 3	July 10 – September 15
TERM 4	October 3 – December 8

VICTORIA

TERM 1	January 27 – April 6
TERM 2	April 24 – June 23
TERM 3	July 10 – September 15
TERM 4	October 2 – December 20

WESTERN AUSTRALIA

TERM 1	February 1 – April 6
TERM 2	April 24 – June 30
TERM 3	July 17 – September 22
TERM 4	October 9 – December 14

NORTHERN TERRITORY

TERM 1	January 30 – April 6
TERM 2	April 17 – June 23
TERM 3	July 17 – September 22
TERM 4	October 9 – December 15

SOUTH AUSTRALIA

TERM 1	January 30 – April 14
TERM 2	May 1 – July 7
TERM 3	July 24 – September 29
TERM 4	October 16 – December 15

TASMANIA

TERM 1	February 8 – April 5
TERM 2	April 26 – July 7
TERM 3	July 25 – September 29
TERM 4	October 16 – December 21

CHECK WITH YOUR SCHOOL
FOR DATES OF PUPIL-FREE DAYS

Budget planner 2023

$$$	WEEKLY	MONTHLY	ANNUALLY
INCOME			
Net salary/wage			
Bonuses (after tax)			
Dividends/income from investments			
Interest			
Other			
TOTAL INCOME			
EXPENDITURE			
HOUSEHOLD			
Rent/mortgage			
Council rates			
Water rates			
Power & heating			
Telephone/internet			
House & contents insurance			
Maintenance/repairs			
Other			
PERSONAL			
Groceries			
Clothing			
Child care			
School fees			
Toiletries/cosmetics/haircare			
Mobile phone			
Superannuation			
Other			
LOANS			
Personal loans			
Credit/store cards			
Other			

$$$	WEEKLY	MONTHLY	ANNUALLY
TRANSPORT			
Train/bus/ferry fares			
Car registration			
Car insurance			
Petrol			
Tolls			
Parking			
Other			
HEALTH			
Doctor/dentist/physio fees			
Health insurance			
Chemist			
Life insurance/income protection			
Other			
ENTERTAINMENT			
Eating out			
Concerts/movies/theatre			
Memberships			
Holidays/hobbies			
Newspapers/books			
Streaming services			
Other			
OTHER			
Gifts			
Donations to charity			
Regular investments			
TOTAL EXPENDITURE			
TOTAL INCOME			
INCOME MINUS EXPENDITURE			

Health checklist

	LOOKING FOR	HOW OFTEN
Eye examination	Vision loss, general eye health and conditions like glaucoma and cataracts.	From age 65 if you notice vision deterioration. People with family history of glaucoma should have regular, comprehensive eye examinations.
Dental	Gum disease, cavities and general decline in dental health.	Once a year for a check-up, or more often if you have gum issues or plaque build-up.
Hearing	Hearing loss.	When you notice hearing damage or have concerns, or annually for those aged 65 and over.
Bone density scan	Osteoporosis, or low bone density.	Consult your GP, especially if you have a family history of osteoporosis or are aged over 50.
Immunisation status	Immunity to influenza, Covid-19, tetanus, rubella and others.	As advised by your GP. Flu shots are available yearly, and are free for those aged over 65.
Cervical Screening Test	Signs of the human papillomavirus (HPV) and cervical cancer.	The Cervical Screening Test has replaced the Pap smear. Your first test is due when you turn 25 or two years after your last Pap smear. If your results are normal, you should continue to be tested every five years after that.
Breast self-examination	Breast changes, lumps, dimpling or thickening of the skin, nipple change or discharge, pain.	Know the normal look and feel of your breasts. If you notice any new or unusual changes, see your GP, particularly if they persist.
Screening mammogram	Breast lumps or changes not evident to the touch.	Every two years from age 50-74, or annually and earlier if at high risk of breast cancer.
Diabetes screening	Elevated blood glucose levels.	Screening is dependent on your individual risk level. Ask your GP for advice.
Skin check	Spots, moles and freckles which are dry, scaly or have smudgy borders.	Self-check on a regular basis and see your GP about any new or changed skin lesions. Get checked opportunistically if you work outdoors.
Bowel cancer screening	Polyps, other signs of bowel cancer.	Faecal occult blood test every two years from age 50. Those with a family history of bowel cancer may need a colonoscopy every two to five years; talk to your GP.
Blood pressure	High blood pressure, which can increase risk of heart disease and stroke; low blood pressure.	Every two years for all adults aged 18 and over, or more often if there's a family history of high blood pressure, stroke or heart disease.
Cholesterol	High LDL (bad cholesterol) and triglycerides, and low HDL (good cholesterol).	Every five years from age 45, or more often if you're at risk of cardiovascular disease. The results, along with your BP results, will be interpreted by your GP in the context of your overall absolute cardiovascular risk.
Body Mass Index	Healthy weight range and waist measurement.	Every two years by your GP or more if part of an identified or increased risk group.

LAST CHECKED	CONTACT	DATE OF APPOINTMENT	COMPLETED
	For more information, visit cancerscreening.gov.au or call 13 15 56		
	BreastScreen Australia: 13 20 50		
	For more information, visit cancerscreening.gov.au or call 1800 118 868		

Aboriginal and Torres Strait Islander people may have different health needs and should discuss these with their GP.

Don't forget

"

I try to look upon my breast cancer journey as a gift, as it enabled me to feel the love of my family and friends as never before. I hope my participation in a clinical trial will help discover more about this disease for the benefit of others, too.

Christine Cole, diagnosed at age 58

let's make a HEALTHY START

Beginning the day feeling stressed and overwhelmed can wreak havoc on our health. Cultivate a calm morning routine by incorporating some (or all) of these beneficial habits.

1 BE PREPARED If mornings are busy, tick off some tasks the night before. Lay out your work clothes, have breakfast ingredients or medications ready on the bench or pack school bags to save time and stress.

2 DRINK SOME WATER A hydration hit first thing can help fight fatigue, prevent headaches, boost the mood and put you in good stead to drink the recommended eight glasses of fluid per day. Keep a glass of water by your bed as a reminder.

3 MOVE YOUR BODY Starting the day with movement – be it yoga, taking the dog for a walk or a gym session – can get the blood flowing, improve your decision-making skills and help ease mental anxiety.

4 EAT A HEALTHY BREAKFAST Begin with a nourishing meal and you'll be more inclined to make healthy choices as the day goes on. Aim for a mix of lean protein (eggs, milk or Greek yoghurt), healthy fats (avocado or nut butters) and fibre (oats, chia, fruit or vegetables).

5 STEP AWAY FROM YOUR PHONE If you check the news, social media or emails as soon as you open your eyes, you'll likely begin the day in a reactive or defensive mindset. Try keeping your phone away from your bedroom or waiting at least one hour before you check it.

6 MAKE YOUR BED A tidy space helps you feel in control, and can set you on an upwards trajectory of accomplishment. Take it further by washing your breakfast dishes, folding your pyjamas or wiping down the bathroom basin after use.

7 TAKE TIME TO BREATHE Spend five minutes meditating to calm your mind. Set a timer, close your eyes and focus on your breathing as you take long, deep breaths, in and out. You can download a meditation app for further guidance.

8 PUT YOUR NEEDS FIRST If you have children, a partner or an elderly parent to care for, you'll be better equipped to do so if your needs have already been met. This may mean getting up a little earlier to exercise, shower or get dressed before they wake.

9 WRITE A TO-DO LIST Jot down all of the tasks floating around inside your mind. Identify the must-dos (no more than five or it becomes overwhelming) and list them in priority order. You'll feel a sense of pride and purpose as you cross off each one.

10 SLEEP TIGHT
A well-rested mind and body can set you up for a good day. Aim for a reasonable and consistent bedtime, avoid drinking caffeine or alcohol in the hours before bed and create a sleeping environment that's cool, quiet, void of all screens and as dark as possible.

DECEMBER

S	M	T	W	T	F	S
				1	2	3
4	5	6	7	8	9	10
11	12	13	14	15	16	17
18	19	20	21	22	23	24
25	26	27	28	29	30	31

JANUARY

S	M	T	W	T	F	S
1	2	3	4	5	6	7
8	9	10	11	12	13	14
15	16	17	18	19	20	21
22	23	24	25	26	27	28
29	30	31				

FEBRUARY

S	M	T	W	T	F	S
			1	2	3	4
5	6	7	8	9	10	11
12	13	14	15	16	17	18
19	20	21	22	23	24	25
26	27	28				

26 MONDAY   BOXING DAY, PROCLAMATION DAY (SA)

27 TUESDAY   CHRISTMAS DAY HOLIDAY

28 WEDNESDAY

29 THURSDAY

December – January
2022-23

30 FRIDAY

31 SATURDAY <small>NEW YEAR'S EVE</small>

USE THIS WEEK TO REFLECT ON THE YEAR THAT WAS. What are you most proud of? What new goals would you like to work towards in 2023? Write down these thoughts to stay accountable.

1 SUNDAY <small>NEW YEAR'S DAY</small>

	DECEMBER					
S	M	T	W	T	F	S
				1	2	3
4	5	6	7	8	9	10
11	12	13	14	15	16	17
18	19	20	21	22	23	24
25	26	27	28	29	30	31

	JANUARY					
S	M	T	W	T	F	S
1	2	3	4	5	6	7
8	9	10	11	12	13	14
15	16	17	18	19	20	21
22	23	24	25	26	27	28
29	30	31				

	FEBRUARY					
S	M	T	W	T	F	S
			1	2	3	4
5	6	7	8	9	10	11
12	13	14	15	16	17	18
19	20	21	22	23	24	25
26	27	28				

2 MONDAY   NEW YEAR'S DAY HOLIDAY

3 TUESDAY

4 WEDNESDAY

5 THURSDAY

January
2023

6 FRIDAY

7 SATURDAY

8 SUNDAY

			DECEMBER			
S	M	T	W	T	F	S
				1	2	3
4	5	6	7	8	9	10
11	12	13	14	15	16	17
18	19	20	21	22	23	24
25	26	27	28	29	30	31

			JANUARY			
S	M	T	W	T	F	S
1	2	3	4	5	6	7
8	9	10	11	12	13	14
15	16	17	18	19	20	21
22	23	24	25	26	27	28
29	30	31				

			FEBRUARY			
S	M	T	W	T	F	S
			1	2	3	4
5	6	7	8	9	10	11
12	13	14	15	16	17	18
19	20	21	22	23	24	25
26	27	28				

9 MONDAY

10 TUESDAY

11 WEDNESDAY

12 THURSDAY

January
2023

13 FRIDAY

14 SATURDAY

15 SUNDAY

	DECEMBER					
S	M	T	W	T	F	S
					1	2	3
4	5	6	7	8	9	10
11	12	13	14	15	16	17
18	19	20	21	22	23	24
25	26	27	28	29	30	31

	JANUARY					
S	M	T	W	T	F	S
1	2	3	4	5	6	7
8	9	10	11	12	13	14
15	16	17	18	19	20	21
22	23	24	25	26	27	28
29	30	31				

	FEBRUARY					
S	M	T	W	T	F	S
				1	2	3	4
5	6	7	8	9	10	11
12	13	14	15	16	17	18
19	20	21	22	23	24	25
26	27	28				

16 MONDAY

17 TUESDAY

18 WEDNESDAY

19 THURSDAY

20 FRIDAY

21 SATURDAY

LISTEN TO SOME MUSIC. Start your day feeling happy and energised by playing upbeat tunes while you brush your teeth, take a shower or drive to work.

22 SUNDAY LUNAR NEW YEAR

DECEMBER

S	M	T	W	T	F	S
				1	2	3
4	5	6	7	8	9	10
11	12	13	14	15	16	17
18	19	20	21	22	23	24
25	26	27	28	29	30	31

JANUARY

S	M	T	W	T	F	S
1	2	3	4	5	6	7
8	9	10	11	12	13	14
15	16	17	18	19	20	21
22	23	24	25	26	27	28
29	30	31				

FEBRUARY

S	M	T	W	T	F	S
			1	2	3	4
5	6	7	8	9	10	11
12	13	14	15	16	17	18
19	20	21	22	23	24	25
26	27	28				

23 MONDAY

24 TUESDAY

25 WEDNESDAY

26 THURSDAY AUSTRALIA DAY

January
2023

27 FRIDAY

28 SATURDAY

COMMUTING TO WORK? Use your bus or train trip to indulge in some self-care. Listen to a podcast, do some knitting or drawing, or read a chapter of a book.

29 SUNDAY

66

I felt like I was on a treadmill that wasn't slowing down. So much information to process, it was overwhelming, sad and confusing. At times I was calm and centred, other times lost with no direction. When I knew more about what the treatment plan was, things got better.

**Sue McGregor,
diagnosed at age 50**

let's talk about
BEING ACTIVE

With much of our lives spent sitting still, daily exercise and movement is essential. Break the sedentary cycle to enjoy improved energy levels, better sleep, stronger muscles, increased balance and less stress.

No matter how old you are, moving your body every day can do wonders for your physical health and mental wellbeing. The amount and type of exercise you need will differ, so read on for recommendations relevant to your age and life stage.

KIDS AND TEENS

The guidelines: From ages one to 17, build one to three hours of moderate to vigorous activity into each day. From age five, try to include activities that strengthen muscle and bone (climbing, push-ups, sit-ups, running) three times a week.

Put it into practice: Encourage children to move more by setting a positive example yourself. Be active together by going for bush walks or bike rides, visiting a local park or playground, working in the garden or washing the car. Organised activities like team sports, dance classes or martial arts are great for teaching new skills.

ADULTS 18-64 YEARS

The guidelines: Minimise long periods of sitting and aim for between 2.5 and 5 hours of moderate activity over the week or 1.5 to 2.5 hours of vigorous activity – or a mixture of both. It's also recommended you incorporate some form of strength training at least twice a week.

Put it into practice: Find something you enjoy and try to do it regularly, at a time that suits you. Team sports, running and cycling are great forms of vigorous activity, while squats, lunges or push-ups count as strength training. To avoid muscle strain or injury, balance high-intensity workouts with low-impact, moderate options like yoga, Pilates, walking and swimming.

ADULTS 65 YEARS AND OVER

The guidelines: Try for at least 30 minutes of moderate activity on most (if not all) days. Include activities that focus on strength and balance (lifting, carrying, climbing stairs) at least three days per week.

Put it into practice: If you've stayed active over the years, you can continue to enjoy a range of exercises and activities. But if you suffer from a chronic illness or medical condition that affects your mobility or have been sedentary for some time, see your doctor before beginning a new exercise routine. Walking, swimming, cycling, Tai Chi, yoga and golf are all relatively safe options. In addition, try to continue doing household tasks like mowing, washing the car and vacuuming for as long as you can.

Simple ways to improve posture

It's well known that a sedentary lifestyle can be bad for our health, and one obvious sign of this is poor posture. Sitting in front of computer screens, looking down at our phones or slouching on the couch to watch TV can cause tension through the back and neck. It can also have a detrimental effect on our posture – and health. Thankfully, making adjustments to the way we hold our bodies can prevent this.

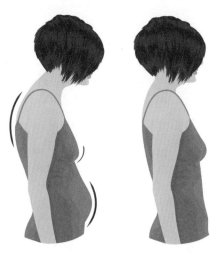

What constitutes 'good' or 'bad' posture?
If you look at a young child, their spine has a graceful S-shaped curve and they move easily and effortlessly. This is the definition of good posture. Signs of poor posture include rounded or hunched shoulders, a head that leans forward and/or a pot belly. To adjust yours, straighten your back, roll your shoulders back and down and lift your head with your chin pointing forward. Adjust your pelvis to hold in your tummy and balance your weight between your feet. When sitting, feet should rest flat on the floor.

Why is posture so important?
When we sit or stand in proper alignment, our muscles, bones and joints can function the way they're meant to. We feel better, have more energy and are less susceptible to muscle and joint pain, stiffness, poor circulation, headaches and digestive issues.

HOW CAN I IMPROVE MY POSTURE?

Exercise regularly to increase muscle tone and strength and reduce the damage of sedentary behaviours

Do mobility/flexibility exercises regularly to help maintain range of movement

Rest feet flat on the floor when sitting, or cross legs at the ankle

Get up from your desk every hour to move

Avoid low-seated, cushioned couches in favour of firmer, more supportive armchairs

Use a lumbar roll to support your lower back when working at a desk or driving for long periods

Hold your phone up in front of you rather than in your lap when looking at it for long periods

Carry bags between both arms to evenly distribute the weight, or use a backpack.

For more information, visit Exercise & Sports Science Australia; exerciseright.com.au

Discover the joys of dance

Dance is an excellent and enjoyable form of exercise that women of all ages and experience levels can take part in. Just some of the associated health benefits include: increased aerobic fitness; improved muscle tone and strength; better coordination, flexibility, balance and endurance; stronger bones; reduced feelings of isolation; improved mood; a reduced risk of dementia; and greater sense of achievement and satisfaction.

You can dance socially or competitively, on your own or with a friend or partner. Look for classes on offer at local dance schools, fitness clubs, community halls or social venues, or once you've got the basics down pat, dance at home.

Wondering which dance style to try? Consider your physical ability, interests, budget and reasons for trying dance with help from these prompts at right.

I WANT...	TRY...
To dance alone	Ballet, samba, hula, tap dance
To dance with a partner	Salsa, swing, ballroom
To dance as part of a group	Line dancing, theatre jazz, acrobatic dance
To perform for others	Burlesque, jazz, Bollywood
To build my strength	Latin dance, pole dancing, contemporary
To lose weight	Zumba, DanceFit
Something slow	Waltz, bolero, lyrical jazz
Something fast-paced	Jive, Zumba, Latin funk, Afro-fusion
Something sensual	Belly dancing, pole dancing, rumba
Something with a beat	Tap dance, flamenco, Irish dance
Something that's easy to pick up	Merengue, ballroom

10 ways to factor exercise into your day

If you lead a busy life, fitting in at least 30 minutes of exercise a day can seem like a daunting task. Take the stress out of meeting this daily goal with these easy-to-achieve suggestions.

1 **Exercise early in the morning** before you get busy. Set your alarm half an hour earlier than your usual wake-up time or before your family wakes up.

2 **Skip the online grocery order** and head to the supermarket in person, parking at the far end of the carpark for extra steps. If you only need a few items, leave the car at home. For an added arm workout, use a basket instead of a trolley.

3 **Plan active catch-ups with friends.** Play a game of tennis or golf, go for a bush walk, form a social netball or soccer team or try something new like indoor rock climbing.

4 **Exercise while your kids are at sports training.** Walk or run laps of the perimeter or utilise outdoor gym equipment to do a circuit of lunges, dips and push-ups.

5 **Combine exercise with typical 'downtime' activities.** For example, lift small weights while watching TV.

6 **Walk or cycle to work,** or get off a stop or two early if you catch public transport.

7 **Always take a lunch break** (even if working from home) and use it to go for a walk or run or do a gym class.

8 **Plan a date with your partner that gets your heart pumping** in more ways than one. Try dance lessons, a walk on the beach, kayaking or ice skating.

9 **Download some online workouts** that can be done at home whenever you have a free window – while dinner's in the oven, when your partner or children are having their showers or just before bed.

10 **Play with your kids or grandkids.** Push them on the swings, play tip, throw a frisbee, start a game of backyard cricket or jump on the trampoline to work those muscles and increase your heart rate.

WHY I SUPPORT BREAST CANCER CLINICAL TRIALS

PROFESSOR BRUCE MANN
DIRECTOR OF RESEARCH,
BREAST CANCER TRIALS

BREAST CANCER IS THE MOST COMMONLY DIAGNOSED CANCER IN WOMEN WORLDWIDE. I see the impact of this every day in my clinics where I meet women and their families who are navigating the challenges, both physical and emotional, of a breast cancer diagnosis.

What treatments are available to them is directly related to the evidence provided in a clinical trial. This is why breast cancer clinical trials research is so important – we must provide every patient with the treatment choice that will give them the best chance of long-term cure, and which avoids unwanted side effects.

During my professional career as a surgeon and member of Breast Cancer Trials, I have witnessed the significant advances made in the treatment of breast cancer over the past 25 years, which has led to more lives saved with reduced treatment side effects.

However, despite advances made, more solutions are urgently needed. It is for all those we miss and who are never forgotten that we must keep up the momentum.

BREAST CANCER TRIALS

LIKE TO KEEP UP TO DATE ON THE LATEST BREAST CANCER RESEARCH AND RESULTS?

Sign up to receive our monthly e-newsletter at breastcancertrials. org.au/diary-newsletter-sign-up or scan this QR code.

JANUARY						
S	M	T	W	T	F	S
1	2	3	4	5	6	7
8	9	10	11	12	13	14
15	16	17	18	19	20	21
22	23	24	25	26	27	28
29	30	31				

FEBRUARY						
S	M	T	W	T	F	S
			1	2	3	4
5	6	7	8	9	10	11
12	13	14	15	16	17	18
19	20	21	22	23	24	25
26	27	28				

MARCH						
S	M	T	W	T	F	S
			1	2	3	4
5	6	7	8	9	10	11
12	13	14	15	16	17	18
19	20	21	22	23	24	25
26	27	28	29	30	31	

30 MONDAY

31 TUESDAY

1 WEDNESDAY

2 THURSDAY

February
2023

3 FRIDAY

4 SATURDAY

MAKE WEEKLY EXERCISE APPOINTMENTS. Block off two or three hours in your diary and treat them like meetings or medical appointments that can't be missed.

5 SUNDAY

JANUARY						
S	M	T	W	T	F	S
1	2	3	4	5	6	7
8	9	10	11	12	13	14
15	16	17	18	19	20	21
22	23	24	25	26	27	28
29	30	31				

FEBRUARY						
S	M	T	W	T	F	S
			1	2	3	4
5	6	7	8	9	10	11
12	13	14	15	16	17	18
19	20	21	22	23	24	25
26	27	28				

MARCH						
S	M	T	W	T	F	S
			1	2	3	4
5	6	7	8	9	10	11
12	13	14	15	16	17	18
19	20	21	22	23	24	25
26	27	28	29	30	31	

6 MONDAY

7 TUESDAY

8 WEDNESDAY

9 THURSDAY

February
2023

10 FRIDAY

11 SATURDAY

> **TRACK YOUR EXERCISE PROGRESS** to ensure ongoing success. Use an app to record walks or runs, keep a journal or invest in a fitness watch that counts steps.

12 SUNDAY

JANUARY
S	M	T	W	T	F	S
1	2	3	4	5	6	7
8	9	10	11	12	13	14
15	16	17	18	19	20	21
22	23	24	25	26	27	28
29	30	31				

FEBRUARY
S	M	T	W	T	F	S
			1	2	3	4
5	6	7	8	9	10	11
12	13	14	15	16	17	18
19	20	21	22	23	24	25
26	27	28				

MARCH
S	M	T	W	T	F	S
			1	2	3	4
5	6	7	8	9	10	11
12	13	14	15	16	17	18
19	20	21	22	23	24	25
26	27	28	29	30	31	

13 MONDAY

14 TUESDAY VALENTINE'S DAY

15 WEDNESDAY

16 THURSDAY

17 FRIDAY

18 SATURDAY ISRA AND MI'RAJ (ISLAMIC HOLY DAY), MAHA SHIVRATRI (HINDU FESTIVAL)

STAY HYDRATED WHILE YOU EXERCISE. We can lose 1.5 litres of fluid for every hour of physical activity, causing fatigue, cramps and a drop in performance.

19 SUNDAY

JANUARY

S	M	T	W	T	F	S
1	2	3	4	5	6	7
8	9	10	11	12	13	14
15	16	17	18	19	20	21
22	23	24	25	26	27	28
29	30	31				

FEBRUARY

S	M	T	W	T	F	S
			1	2	3	4
5	6	7	8	9	10	11
12	13	14	15	16	17	18
19	20	21	22	23	24	25
26	27	28				

MARCH

S	M	T	W	T	F	S
			1	2	3	4
5	6	7	8	9	10	11
12	13	14	15	16	17	18
19	20	21	22	23	24	25
26	27	28	29	30	31	

20 MONDAY

21 TUESDAY

22 WEDNESDAY

23 THURSDAY

February
2023

24 FRIDAY

25 SATURDAY

> **DUST OFF YOUR BIKE!** Cycling is a fantastic form of aerobic activity that can assist in strengthening the heart, lungs and blood vessels. It's also good for the environment.

26 SUNDAY

Breast cancer continues to affect you emotionally long after the treatment is completed. I longed for the time when I wouldn't think about it every day. Eventually life returns to normal. Today I am healthy, happy and enjoying my gorgeous grandchildren. Life is good.

Cathy Ingham, diagnosed at age 48, pictured with her husband and grandchildren

let's talk about
NUTRITION

Eating a varied, healthy diet has many benefits, from fuelling our bodies with energy, to protecting us from illness and disease and improving memory and mood. Make nutritious choices daily to reap the rewards.

Tiredness is such a common experience that many people brush off as a normal symptom of a busy lifestyle. And while stress, burnout and a lack of sleep can be part of the problem, inadequate diet also plays a role. Here, we list the dietary choices that could be contributing to your fatigue.

WHAT'S CAUSING THOSE ENERGY SLUMPS?

Skipping meals or eating at irregular times causes our blood glucose levels to drop and reduces our intake of essential vitamins and minerals. Instead, eat a moderate-sized meal or high-protein/low-GI snack every two to three hours to give your body a constant stream of energy.

Not enough fruit and vegetables. Our bodies can't function efficiently without the right mix of vitamins and minerals. It's recommended we eat two serves of fruit and five serves of vegetables each day for this reason. Aim to eat a variety of different coloured options throughout the day.

A lack of iron or protein. Iron helps transport oxygen to the brain and muscles, while protein is a good source of energy to keep us feeling full for longer. Both can be found in lean meat, poultry, fish, nuts, seeds, eggs, tofu, legumes and beans.

Too many refined carbohydrates and sugars. Indulging in sugary snacks can lead to a spike in blood glucose levels, followed by a slump. Break the cycle by opting for slow-release carbohydrates or healthy fats found in wholegrains, legumes, nuts and seeds and avocado.

Dehydration. If we don't drink enough fluids, our blood volume drops, forcing the heart to work harder to pump oxygen and nutrients around the body. Aim for 2 litres of water a day – more in hot weather.

Too much caffeine. As a stimulant, caffeine (coffee, tea, cola, energy drinks) provides a temporary energy boost, followed by a dip as the effects wear off. It can also disturb your sleep. Cap your consumption at two cups per day, and avoid having any caffeine after 2pm.

Not eating enough. When we eat too few calories, our body lacks the energy to function properly, leading to fatigue. Aim for at least 1200 to 1800 calories per day.

For more information, visit Nutrition Australia; nutritionaustralia.org

Eat your way to wellness

Cold and flu season is almost upon us. Set yourself up for wellness by incorporating a range of immunity-boosting plant foods into your weekly meal plan, including these.

CITRUS FRUITS Vitamin C is thought to increase our white blood cell count to help fight infection. Add a slice, squeeze or wedge of orange, lemon or lime to every meal.

GARLIC Prized for its germ-fighting capabilities and healthy heart benefits, garlic is extremely versatile and is used in almost every global cuisine.

BROCCOLI With antioxidants, vitamins, minerals and fibre, broccoli (or cabbage, brussels sprouts and broccolini) is best served steamed or raw to retain its nutrients.

RED CAPSICUM It's a rich source of vitamin A, to help keep the mouth, stomach, intestines and respiratory system tissue healthy. Try capsicum sticks with dip.

SPINACH Another good form of vitamin C, it also contains antioxidants, folate and beta-carotene, which may increase the body's infection-fighting abilities.

YOGHURT Look for 'live active cultures' on the label. These good bacteria or probiotics can help protect against disease and enhance immune function.

OILY FISH The omega-3s in salmon, mackerel, tuna and sardines can improve immune function by reducing inflammation, while vitamin D helps fight infection.

SHELLFISH Zinc improves immune system function, and oysters, crab and lobster are all high in it. But don't overdo it – more than 8mg per day can have the reverse effect.

PAPAYA Loaded with folate, vitamin C, potassium and magnesium, papaya also contains a digestive enzyme called papain, which has anti-inflammatory benefits.

TRY THESE IDEAS:

Fruit
A piece of fruit
Mixed berries
Fruit salad
Canned fruit in juice

Vegetables
Vegetable sticks with dip
(hummus, tzatziki or salsa)
Vegetable muffin
Corn on the cob
A small cup of minestrone
or pumpkin soup

Dairy and alternatives
Cheese served with
wholegrain crackers
A tub of yoghurt or custard
(check the sugar content)
Small smoothie
Edamame beans

Grains
Air-popped popcorn
Rice cakes or crispbread
with ricotta, nut butter
or avocado
A slice of wholegrain
fruit toast
Wholegrain cereal with milk

Protein
Boiled eggs
Zucchini slice or frittata
A handful of raw almonds,
hazelnuts or walnuts
Tuna on crackers

The healthy guide to snacking

Despite contradictory reports, snacking between meals is encouraged by nutritionists. Fuelling your body with healthy snacks helps maintain energy levels between meals, provides a good opportunity to eat more fruit, veg, protein and fibre, and stops you from getting too hungry later in the day. Avoid processed, pre-packaged snacks, which can be high in refined sugars, salt and saturated fat, and instead look for options from the five food groups.

The pros and cons of meal-delivery services

If life is busy, you live on your own or lack the motivation to cook every day, pre-prepared meals are a convenient option. Many options are much better for you than takeaway or toast every night, but it pays to weigh up the benefits against any potential disadvantages.

THE PROS	THE CONS
CONVENIENCE	**THE COST**
The weekly tasks of meal planning and shopping for ingredients are taken care of for you, which is a godsend for those who are time-poor or not very mobile.	Comparisons have shown that shopping for ingredients at the supermarket costs significantly less than having your meals delivered on a regular basis.
LESS THINKING REQUIRED	**SOME PLANNING IS STILL NEEDED**
If meal planning has become a chore and you dread the daily 'what's for dinner?' question, meal-delivery services can help alleviate this stress.	You'll need to plan ahead and remember to select your meals each week. You can pause deliveries when they're not needed, as long as you do so before a set deadline.
MINIMAL PREP TIME	**YOU STILL HAVE TO SHOP**
All meal-kit ingredients are supplied in correct measurements, with easy-to-follow recipe cards. Pre-prepared meals just need to be heated in the microwave.	While some meals are covered, you'll need to shop for incidental items like tea, coffee, milk, fruit, school lunch ingredients, snacks and other household essentials.
LESS FOOD WASTE	**EXCESS PACKAGING**
Meal kits give you all the ingredients needed for the number of serves you ordered, as opposed to buying a whole head of lettuce or bottle of sauce.	The downside of those carefully portioned ingredients is the packaging. Some items can be recycled or returned with your next delivery, while others will go to landfill.
IT'S HEALTHIER THAN TAKEAWAY	**NOT ALWAYS GOOD FOR YOU**
Many meal kits use fresh ingredients with an emphasis on vegetables and grains. Look for 2.5 to 3 serves of vegetables. There are also gluten-free and calorie-controlled options.	Some meals can be high in fat, sugar and salt, and not recommended for those with high blood pressure or cholesterol. Always read nutrition panels and ingredient lists.
GREAT FOR SINGLES AND COUPLES	**EXPENSIVE FOR FAMILIES**
Cooking for one every night can lose its appeal, while competing schedules makes meal-planning difficult. Having a few meals in the fridge or freezer can fill those gaps.	Most meal-kit plans only cater for two or four serves, with some serving sizes on the small side for men and teenagers. You may need to bulk up meals with additional ingredients.
YOU'LL GET SOME POINTERS	**LACK OF EDUCATION**
Meal-kit services can teach you about portion control, expose you to new recipes and provide ideas for incorporating more vegetables into your meals.	In the case of pre-prepared meals, having all the cooking done for you means you'll gain little knowledge about healthy ingredients or cooking methods.

Healthy drink swaps

Having a cup of coffee in the morning or glass of wine at night may be a comforting ritual, but this daily refreshment can be detrimental to our health if we overindulge. In large doses (more than two espresso shots or five teaspoons of instant coffee per day), caffeine can contribute to anxiety, irritability and sleeplessness. And having more than 10 standard drinks of alcohol per week (or more than four in one sitting) can lead to cardiovascular disease, diabetes, obesity and depression. Reduce your alcohol and caffeine intake with these alternatives.

CAFFEINE-FREE OPTIONS
Herbal tea Try peppermint to aid digestion, ginger to relieve nausea, rose hip for antioxidants or chamomile to help you sleep.
Dandelion coffee Prescribed for its anti-inflammatory benefits, it has a slightly nutty flavour with a bitter aftertaste like coffee.
Golden turmeric latte A blend of turmeric, milk, pepper, ginger, cardamom, honey and cinnamon, with anti-inflammatory benefits.

ALCOHOL-FREE OPTIONS
Virgin strawberry mojito Combine ¼ cup coconut water, ½ cup sliced strawberries, 6 mint leaves, 1 tbsp lime juice and ½ tbsp honey in a blender and blitz. Pour into a glass and top with ½ cup soda water.
Soda and lime As simple as it sounds: add a few lime wedges to a glass of iced soda water and top up as often as you like.
Cranberry juice and soda Pour equal parts soda water to cranberry juice and finish with a lime wedge.
Kombucha Packed with probiotics for gut health. Look for options without artificial sweeteners, or even better, make your own.

FEBRUARY

S	M	T	W	T	F	S
			1	2	3	4
5	6	7	8	9	10	11
12	13	14	15	16	17	18
19	20	21	22	23	24	25
26	27	28				

MARCH

S	M	T	W	T	F	S
			1	2	3	4
5	6	7	8	9	10	11
12	13	14	15	16	17	18
19	20	21	22	23	24	25
26	27	28	29	30	31	

APRIL

S	M	T	W	T	F	S
30						1
2	3	4	5	6	7	8
9	10	11	12	13	14	15
16	17	18	19	20	21	22
23	24	25	26	27	28	29

27 MONDAY

28 TUESDAY

1 WEDNESDAY

2 THURSDAY

March
2023

3 FRIDAY

4 SATURDAY

> **OVEREATING CAN MAKE YOU TIRED** and lethargic. Practise mindful eating by chewing each bite slowly and paying attention to signals from your body that it's satisfied or full.

5 SUNDAY

	FEBRUARY							MARCH							APRIL					
S	M	T	W	T	F	S	S	M	T	W	T	F	S	S	M	T	W	T	F	S
			1	2	3	4				1	2	3	4	30						1
5	6	7	8	9	10	11	5	6	7	8	9	10	11	2	3	4	5	6	7	8
12	13	14	15	16	17	18	12	13	14	15	16	17	18	9	10	11	12	13	14	15
19	20	21	22	23	24	25	19	20	21	22	23	24	25	16	17	18	19	20	21	22
26	27	28					26	27	28	29	30	31		23	24	25	26	27	28	29

6 MONDAY LABOUR DAY (WA)

7 TUESDAY

8 WEDNESDAY INTERNATIONAL WOMEN'S DAY

9 THURSDAY

March
2023

10 FRIDAY

11 SATURDAY

12 SUNDAY

FEBRUARY

S	M	T	W	T	F	S
			1	2	3	4
5	6	7	8	9	10	11
12	13	14	15	16	17	18
19	20	21	22	23	24	25
26	27	28				

MARCH

S	M	T	W	T	F	S
			1	2	3	4
5	6	7	8	9	10	11
12	13	14	15	16	17	18
19	20	21	22	23	24	25
26	27	28	29	30	31	

APRIL

S	M	T	W	T	F	S
30						1
2	3	4	5	6	7	8
9	10	11	12	13	14	15
16	17	18	19	20	21	22
23	24	25	26	27	28	29

13 MONDAY ADELAIDE CUP (SA), CANBERRA DAY (ACT), EIGHT HOURS DAY (TAS), LABOUR DAY (VIC)

14 TUESDAY

15 WEDNESDAY

16 THURSDAY NATIONAL CLOSE THE GAP DAY

March
2023

17 FRIDAY ST PATRICK'S DAY, HOLI (HINDU FESTIVAL)

18 SATURDAY

19 SUNDAY

FEBRUARY						
S	M	T	W	T	F	S
			1	2	3	4
5	6	7	8	9	10	11
12	13	14	15	16	17	18
19	20	21	22	23	24	25
26	27	28				

MARCH						
S	M	T	W	T	F	S
			1	2	3	4
5	6	7	8	9	10	11
12	13	14	15	16	17	18
19	20	21	22	23	24	25
26	27	28	29	30	31	

APRIL						
S	M	T	W	T	F	S
30						1
2	3	4	5	6	7	8
9	10	11	12	13	14	15
16	17	18	19	20	21	22
23	24	25	26	27	28	29

20 MONDAY

21 TUESDAY   HARMONY DAY, NOWRUZ (PERSIAN NEW YEAR)

22 WEDNESDAY

23 THURSDAY   RAMADAN BEGINS

March
2023

24 FRIDAY

25 SATURDAY

MANY PACKAGED SNACKS COME in serving sizes that are larger than what we actually need. As a guide, try to keep your snack serves to less than 600 kilojoules.

26 SUNDAY

FEBRUARY

S	M	T	W	T	F	S
			1	2	3	4
5	6	7	8	9	10	11
12	13	14	15	16	17	18
19	20	21	22	23	24	25
26	27	28				

MARCH

S	M	T	W	T	F	S
			1	2	3	4
5	6	7	8	9	10	11
12	13	14	15	16	17	18
19	20	21	22	23	24	25
26	27	28	29	30	31	

APRIL

S	M	T	W	T	F	S
30						1
2	3	4	5	6	7	8
9	10	11	12	13	14	15
16	17	18	19	20	21	22
23	24	25	26	27	28	29

27 MONDAY

28 TUESDAY

29 WEDNESDAY

30 THURSDAY

March-April
2023

31 FRIDAY

1 SATURDAY

> **ZINC DEFICIENCY IS LINKED** with memory loss, low concentration and an inability to make decisions. Chicken, fish, seafood, red meat, nuts, dairy and legumes are all good sources.

2 SUNDAY

> Prior to my diagnosis I took my life for granted. I enjoy every single day now. Charlotte took my news pretty hard. This photo shows how happy and healthy we are now following my breast cancer treatment.

Lee Vout, diagnosed at age 52, pictured with her daughter Charlotte

let's talk about
WOMEN'S HEALTH

Arm yourself with information on the health conditions that affect women most, while also preparing for all of life's stages – from menstruation to pregnancy and eventually menopause.

Menopause is a normal part of ageing that most women will experience, but misinformation and misconceptions can see many of us fear or dread this life stage. Here we sort fact from fiction to help you prepare for the realities of menopause.

MYTH: Menopause begins at 50
TRUTH: In Australia, the average age for menopause is 51 or 52, however, it can occur any time between the ages of 45 and 55. The perimenopausal stage, when periods become irregular and menopausal symptoms are most prominent, can take place some years prior to menopause. In addition, some women will undergo medically induced menopause or early menopause due to treatment (such as chemotherapy), while others will experience premature menopause before 40 or late menopause up to the age of 60.

MYTH: Menopause causes weight gain
TRUTH: Yes, weight gain often coincides with menopause, but there can be other contributing factors as well. As we age, our metabolism slows, affecting our ability to lose weight and decreasing our energy for exercise. A lack of fitness, medications,

family history and poor lifestyle choices (hello, fast food!) can all result in weight gain. To help manage your weight after menopause, aim to incorporate 150 minutes of brisk activity into your week, eat small but frequent meals and reduce alcohol intake.

MYTH: Menopause can't be treated
TRUTH: If menopause symptoms are affecting your quality of life, your GP may recommend Menopausal Hormone Therapy (MHT). In some instances, you may also be able to ease certain symptoms. Reducing caffeine, alcohol and spicy food intake is thought to reduce the severity of hot flushes, or try wearing light, breathable clothing and carrying a handheld fan. Exercise and mindfulness may help with mood swings and irritability.

MYTH: Your sex drive will disappear
TRUTH: Fluctuating hormone levels may cause a drop in libido or vaginal dryness, both of which can be treated with herbal and complementary therapies, MHT or prescription medications. However, some women report an *increased* sex drive during menopause, often linked to greater freedoms after children move out of home or less concerns around falling pregnant.

For more information, visit the Australasian Menopause Society; menopause.org.au

Sustainable period products to try

The average woman will use around 12,000 pads or tampons in her lifetime, which equates to approximately 120kg of waste going into landfill. Thankfully, a number of eco-friendly and reusable feminine products now exist. Read on to discover the alternatives.

PERIOD UNDERWEAR

With the look and feel of normal underwear, period briefs have a built-in absorbent layer to soak up menstrual blood. Choose from high-cut, low-cut and G-string options, which can be worn for up to eight hours. To clean, rinse in cold water and add to your washing machine on a gentle cycle, or handwash in warm water with a mild detergent.

REUSABLE PADS

Made from washable cotton or other natural fibres for greater comfort and breathability. Wash them the same way as period underwear (add a good stain remover, but avoid scented detergents and fabric softeners). If you take good care of them, each pad can last up to three years.

MENSTRUAL CUPS

Made of latex or silicone, menstrual cups resemble a funnel and insert into the vagina like a tampon to collect the menstrual blood. They can be worn for up to eight hours. Once full, simply remove, pour the blood down the toilet, rinse and reuse. Be sure to choose the right size for your flow.

BIODEGRADABLE PADS & TAMPONS

If reusable options don't appeal, try sanitary items made from organic, biodegradable materials. Usually cotton or bamboo with a plant-based backing, they're free of chemicals, synthetics and dyes, and feel more comfortable to wear. Being biodegradable, they'll break down sooner than other products containing plastic.

3 steps to a healthy pregnancy

Expecting a baby? Follow these simple guidelines to give yourself the best chance of a complication-free pregnancy and birth, a straightforward recovery and a healthy baby.

1 Eat plenty of nutritious food

Forget the notion of eating for two and enjoy nutrient-rich meals instead. Aim for a good mix of lean protein, wholegrains and plenty of fresh fruit and vegetables, and at least two healthy snacks a day.

Some foods can cause complications in pregnancy. Avoid deli meats, pate, soft cheeses, raw or undercooked meat or eggs, soft-serve ice cream, smoked salmon, precooked prawns and sushi. Fish that contains high levels of mercury, such as shark, marlin and swordfish, should only be consumed once a fortnight or once a week for orange roughy. All other seafood should be limited to 2-3 serves per week.

Abstain from alcohol and reduce your caffeine intake to 1-2 cups of coffee or 4 cups of tea per day. Also limit high-fat and sugary foods and drinks.

While supplements are no substitute for a healthy diet, taking folic acid while trying to conceive and in the first three months of pregnancy can reduce the risk of your baby developing a neural tube defect such as spina bifida.

3 Prioritise your wellbeing

Fatigue and changes in blood pressure, blood sugar and hormone levels in the first and third trimesters can take a toll on your mental state. Yoga, pregnancy massage, deep breathing and stretching are all wonderful relaxation techniques during pregnancy, while going for a walk or catching up with a friend can instantly lift the mood. Prioritise rest with earlier bedtimes, and ease any discomfort by sleeping on your left side with your knees bent and a pillow under your bump.

Surround yourself with a good support network – your partner, family, friends or neighbours – who can help with household tasks, transport to appointments, child minding or just keep you company. If you're feeling low for more than a few days, it's a good idea to speak to a health professional.

2 Stay physically active

Regular exercise has many proven benefits for mums-to-be, building strength, increasing energy, improving sleep and helping ease pregnancy symptoms of nausea, heartburn and constipation. Aim for at least 30 minutes of moderate-intensity activity each day, checking with a medical professional to ensure your chosen activity is safe for pregnancy. Walking, yoga, swimming, aqua aerobics, Tai Chi and Pilates are all excellent options, but give scuba diving, horse riding, skiing and high-impact sports a miss. Exercise during the cooler parts of the day to avoid overheating, drink plenty of water and stop if you feel unwell, dizzy or have any pain.

Spotlight on endometriosis

THE STATS Endometriosis is a chronic, progressive condition that affects one in nine women. It occurs when tissue similar to the lining of the uterus grows in other parts of the body, including the pelvis and reproductive organs. Approximately 30 per cent of women with endometriosis will have problems falling pregnant. While the exact cause is unknown, in some cases there is a family history of endometriosis.

DIAGNOSIS AND TREATMENT If you think you have endometriosis, your GP can refer you to a gynaecologist. Typically, an ultrasound or laparoscopy (keyhole surgery) is used to detect endometriosis cysts on the ovaries or endometrial tissue within the pelvis. The combined oral contraceptive pill, progestin implants or injections or an intrauterine device (IUD) may be prescribed to reduce the severity of endometriosis and suppress its growth. Surgery is sometimes needed to remove cysts and adhesions, repair scar tissue damage and improve fertility.

SYMPTOMS VARY GREATLY, BUT MAY INCLUDE...

Pain before and during your period, during or after sex or while passing a bowel motion or urinating

Pelvic pain, ovulation pain or back pain

Heavy bleeding with or without clots during menstrual cycle

Irregular or lengthy periods

Extreme tiredness, lethargy and fainting

Constipation, diarrhoea or bloating

Depression, anxiety, mood swings

Inability to fall pregnant.

For more information, visit Endometriosis Australia; endometriosisaustralia.org

Migraine management tips and tricks

Three times an many women as men suffer from debilitating migraines. Along with the severe headache, symptoms include nausea, vomiting, blurry vision, tingling or numbness in the hands and difficulty concentrating. If you suffer from recurring migraines, try these tricks and remedies to help stop them in their tracks.

Turn off the lights. Light and sound can increase a migraine's intensity, so find a dark, quiet room and sleep if you can. Try eye masks, blockout blinds and weighted blankets to create a calm environment.

Experiment with temperature therapy. For some people, cold compresses and ice packs dull the pain, while for others, warm showers or heat packs ease migraine pain. Try both individually or in combination – for example, an ice pack on the back of your neck with your feet in a warm bath.

Hydrate! In a migraine state, the brain overheats and uses more sugars and fluids than usual. Sports drinks like Gatorade or Powerade can help with quick hydration. Iced water, frozen cola or iced coffee may also help if you respond to cold remedies.

Eat well. Plan meals for the same time each day and don't skip meals. Identify any foods that might trigger your migraines, then eliminate them from your diet to see if the frequency or severity lessens.

Go for a walk. If movement and sunlight don't exacerbate your migraines, getting out for a walk can regulate the body and ease nausea. Similarly, floating in a quiet pool can calm the senses and increase blood flow in the brain. Go with a friend so they can watch out for you.

Drink a strong coffee. In small doses, caffeine can relieve migraine pain in the early stages and help boost the effects of painkillers. But don't overdo it – too much caffeine can lead to withdrawal headaches later on and affect your ability to sleep.

For more information, visit Migraine & Headache Australia; headacheaustralia.org.au

		M A R C H				
S	M	T	W	T	F	S
			1	2	3	4
5	6	7	8	9	10	11
12	13	14	15	16	17	18
19	20	21	22	23	24	25
26	27	28	29	30	31	

		A P R I L				
S	M	T	W	T	F	S
30						1
2	3	4	5	6	7	8
9	10	11	12	13	14	15
16	17	18	19	20	21	22
23	24	25	26	27	28	29

		M A Y				
S	M	T	W	T	F	S
	1	2	3	4	5	6
7	8	9	10	11	12	13
14	15	16	17	18	19	20
21	22	23	24	25	26	27
28	29	30	31			

3 MONDAY

4 TUESDAY

5 WEDNESDAY PASSOVER BEGINS

6 THURSDAY

April 2023

7 FRIDAY GOOD FRIDAY

FIND A GOOD GP who listens to you and answers your health concerns. Ask friends and colleagues for recommendations, and help your mum and daughters to find one, too.

8 SATURDAY

9 SUNDAY EASTER SUNDAY

MARCH

S	M	T	W	T	F	S
			1	2	3	4
5	6	7	8	9	10	11
12	13	14	15	16	17	18
19	20	21	22	23	24	25
26	27	28	29	30	31	

APRIL

S	M	T	W	T	F	S
30						1
2	3	4	5	6	7	8
9	10	11	12	13	14	15
16	17	18	19	20	21	22
23	24	25	26	27	28	29

MAY

S	M	T	W	T	F	S
	1	2	3	4	5	6
7	8	9	10	11	12	13
14	15	16	17	18	19	20
21	22	23	24	25	26	27
28	29	30	31			

10 MONDAY EASTER MONDAY

11 TUESDAY EASTER TUESDAY (TAS)

12 WEDNESDAY

13 THURSDAY

April
2023

14 FRIDAY

15 SATURDAY

MOTHER'S DAY IS AROUND THE CORNER. Why not give Mum a gift with meaning by making a donation to breast cancer research on her behalf? Visit breastcancertrials. org.au and get a special Mother's Day card for her.

16 SUNDAY ORTHODOX EASTER

		MARCH				
S	M	T	W	T	F	S
			1	2	3	4
5	6	7	8	9	10	11
12	13	14	15	16	17	18
19	20	21	22	23	24	25
26	27	28	29	30	31	

		APRIL				
S	M	T	W	T	F	S
30						1
2	3	4	5	6	7	8
9	10	11	12	13	14	15
16	17	18	19	20	21	22
23	24	25	26	27	28	29

		MAY				
S	M	T	W	T	F	S
	1	2	3	4	5	6
7	8	9	10	11	12	13
14	15	16	17	18	19	20
21	22	23	24	25	26	27
28	29	30	31			

17 MONDAY

18 TUESDAY

19 WEDNESDAY

20 THURSDAY

April
2023

21 FRIDAY EID AL-FITR (ISLAMIC HOLIDAY)

22 SATURDAY

PRACTICE SELF-CARE AT THE END OF EACH DAY. Listen to a meditation podcast or soothing music, soak in a warm bath, sip a cup of herbal tea, try some gentle yoga poses or read a book.

23 SUNDAY

		MARCH				
S	M	T	W	T	F	S
			1	2	3	4
5	6	7	8	9	10	11
12	13	14	15	16	17	18
19	20	21	22	23	24	25
26	27	28	29	30	31	

		APRIL				
S	M	T	W	T	F	S
30						1
2	3	4	5	6	7	8
9	10	11	12	13	14	15
16	17	18	19	20	21	22
23	24	25	26	27	28	29

		MAY				
S	M	T	W	T	F	S
	1	2	3	4	5	6
7	8	9	10	11	12	13
14	15	16	17	18	19	20
21	22	23	24	25	26	27
28	29	30	31			

24 MONDAY

25 TUESDAY ANZAC DAY

26 WEDNESDAY

27 THURSDAY

April
2023

28 FRIDAY

29 SATURDAY

30 SUNDAY

"

My breast cancer was detected at its earliest stage via the national breast screening program. I could have easily put off having my mammogram because of various reasons. But it's so important to make it a priority. I'm sure it saved my life.

**Kim McCarthy,
diagnosed at age 68**

let's talk about
HEART HEALTH

In Australia, 10 women die from a heart attack each day. Knowing your heart disease risk and making simple lifestyle changes could protect you – and you're never too young or old to start.

Did you know, a daily 30-minute walk is excellent for the heart? Not only does it help manage heart disease risk factors like high blood pressure, cholesterol and weight gain, it can also reduce our risk of stroke and type 2 diabetes. Best of all, walking is a cheap and easy form of exercise for all ages and abilities. Here's how to make walking a part of your routine.

Seek advice

If you have a medical condition that could be affected by physical activity, such as heart disease, high blood pressure, asthma, diabetes or obesity, or have been inactive for some time, speak to your doctor about the safest way to begin walking for exercise.

Do your prep work

Before you even step outside, warm up with some simple calf, hamstring, quadricep and shoulder stretches to prepare the muscles for movement. Wear thick, comfortable socks, season-appropriate clothing and lightweight, supportive sneakers, and don't forget to apply sunscreen and wear a hat if walking during the day. Take a water bottle with you in warm weather or on longer walks, and avoid walking during the hottest part of the day in the peak of summer.

Get started

Build up slowly, starting with 10-15 minutes of walking at a moderate pace, three or four times a week. It's considered moderate if it requires effort, but you can still comfortably hold a conversation. Listen to your body and don't push too hard in the beginning. Once you feel you've mastered this pace, gradually increase your speed, distance and frequency. A vigorous walk will make you breathe harder and faster, and it will be almost impossible to talk without getting puffed. You may like to add some hills to your walk for an added challenge.

Keep going!

You need to walk regularly to get the benefits, so find ways to keep it interesting. Research different scenic walking tracks near you and mix it up – say, a beach walk one day, bush walk the next, then a walk around the block. Use wireless headphones or earbuds to listen to music or podcasts while you walk, or enlist a friend to walk with you. You might like to join a local walking group to meet new people.

Can't manage 30 minutes? Break up your walk into 10-minute increments – for example, walking to the bus stop, doing a few laps around a shopping centre or walking to and from school pick-up.

For more information, visit the Victor Chang Cardiac Research Institute; victorchang.edu.au

Heart disease: the risks for women

Currently, 22 Australian women die from heart disease each day. Our risk increases once we turn 45, or 30 for Aboriginal and Torres Strait Islander women. In addition, 90 per cent of Australian women have at least one risk factor for heart disease. Research shows that women are often under-treated when it comes to heart disease, and that's why it's important to know the risks and how you can mitigate them.

Know your risks

As well as the universal risk factors of high blood pressure, high cholesterol, diabetes, obesity, poor diet, physical inactivity, stress, depression, family history and smoking, the following female-specific contributing factors can increase our risk:

- Taking the oral contraceptive pill in addition to smoking
- Pregnancy complications, such as high blood pressure, pre-eclampsia and gestational diabetes
- Polycystic ovary syndrome (PCOS), which can lead to obesity, high blood pressure, type 2 diabetes and high cholesterol
- Autoimmune diseases, such as multiple sclerosis, lupus and rheumatoid arthritis, which can raise cholesterol levels
- Menopausal changes affecting fat distribution around the mid-section
- Premature menopause before age 45.

Take a proactive approach

If any of the above risk factors are relevant to you, mention them to your doctor as part of your medical history. Your GP will likely conduct a Heart Health Check to determine your risk score and the best ways to reduce it.

In addition, the following lifestyle changes could help reduce your risk:

- Eat a healthy diet that includes plenty of fruit, vegetables, legumes, nuts and seeds, wholegrain cereals, lean protein, oily fish and dairy (reduced-fat varieties if you have high cholesterol).
- Drink lots of water. As a guide, women need about eight cups of fluid a day, or nine if you're pregnant or breastfeeding.
- Aim for 30-45 minutes of moderate-intensity activity each day.
- Reduce alcohol intake to no more than 10 standard drinks per week, and no more than four standard drinks per day.
- Quit smoking. For help, visit quit.org.au or call 137 848.
- Check your blood pressure and cholesterol levels every year, and your blood glucose levels every three years, or as advised by your healthcare provider if you have diabetes.

The warning signs of heart attack and stroke

Only one in three women will experience 'typical' heart attack symptoms, such as pain in the centre of the chest. Instead, they'll have other, more subtle warning signs, which often go ignored. If you or someone you know experiences one or a combination of the symptoms listed here, call Triple Zero (000) immediately.

HEART ATTACK

Pressure or tightness in the chest

Pain, tightness or numbness in the neck, jaw, shoulder, upper back or abdomen

Pain in one or both arms

Shortness of breath

Nausea, vomiting or indigestion

Hot and cold sweats

Light-headedness or dizziness

Unusual feelings of fatigue

Heart palpitations

STROKE

Paralysis, weakness or numbness in the face, arms or legs on one or both sides of the body

Drooping of the face, eyes or mouth on one or both sides

Difficulty speaking or understanding, slurred or garbled speech

Inability to lift one or both arms due to weakness or numbness

Dizziness, loss of balance or an unexplained fall

Loss of vision, sudden blurring or decreased vision in one or both eyes

Severe, abrupt or unexplained headache

Difficulty swallowing

6 simple heart-friendly food swaps

Making small changes to your diet can help reduce common heart-associated issues like weight gain, high blood pressure and diabetes, and you don't need to throw out the entire contents of your pantry to do so. Simply trade one food for another.

1 Swap butter for vegetable oil Butter is a source of saturated fat, which can raise cholesterol levels. Cook with vegetable oils like olive, canola or sunflower, which contain healthy fats, and opt for healthy spreads like avocado, tahini, hummus or nut butters.

2 Swap refined carbohydrates for wholegrains White rice, flour, pasta and bread contain minimal fibre and have a high glycaemic index, which can lead to spikes in blood glucose levels. Switch for grainy breads, wholemeal pasta and flour and brown rice.

3 Swap salt for spices Too much salt can raise your blood pressure, so season with herbs and spices instead. Pair rosemary or garlic with red meat; sage or tarragon with poultry; lemon juice or fennel with fish; chives or chilli with eggs; thyme or onion with vegies.

4 Swap chips for nuts Fancy something crunchy to snack on? Ditch salty, refined pretzels and chips for a handful of mixed nuts. Try almonds, pistachios, walnuts, cashews, pecans or Brazil nuts. Nuts also add protein and crunch to yoghurt, salads and stir-fries.

5 Swap sugar for fruit Foods with added sweeteners can contribute to obesity and heart problems, but fruit contains natural sugars. Top unsweetened cereal with berries, use pre-soaked dates to sweeten baked goods and forgo soft drinks for water.

6 Swap processed meat for lean or plant alternatives Bacon, sausages, sliced meat and hot dogs may contain salt and chemical compounds that can be harmful to our health. Swap for lean chicken, turkey, salmon, tuna, egg, canned beans, lentils, tofu or tempeh.

MAKE EVERY MOMENT BRIGHTER

Interflora is synonymous the world over with the feelings and sentiments that only flowers can evoke.

We make a good moment great, bad ones a little lighter and everyday moments a reason to be thankful. From expressions of love, to celebrations of success; from shared sorrows, to saying "I'm sorry".

For over 65 years we have always been trusted to play a unique part in the lives of our customers. If it's important to you, it's important to us.

Our commitment to excellence in every aspect of our business – from the beauty of a handcrafted floral arrangement to the delivery to your door – has only strengthened during our long and proud history in Australia. And we'll continue to do so, well into the future.

We don't just deliver flowers, but a feeling, a moment and an emotion. Because the act of giving and receiving flowers makes every moment brighter. Always.

#AlwaysInterflora

f InterfloraAustralia
⊚ @Interflora_AU
🐦 @InterfloraAU

APRIL						
S	M	T	W	T	F	S
30						1
2	3	4	5	6	7	8
9	10	11	12	13	14	15
16	17	18	19	20	21	22
23	24	25	26	27	28	29

MAY						
S	M	T	W	T	F	S
	1	2	3	4	5	6
7	8	9	10	11	12	13
14	15	16	17	18	19	20
21	22	23	24	25	26	27
28	29	30	31			

JUNE						
S	M	T	W	T	F	S
				1	2	3
4	5	6	7	8	9	10
11	12	13	14	15	16	17
18	19	20	21	22	23	24
25	26	27	28	29	30	

1 MONDAY LABOUR DAY (QLD), MAY DAY (NT)

2 TUESDAY

3 WEDNESDAY

4 THURSDAY

5 FRIDAY

6 SATURDAY

**DONATE TO
BREAST CANCER
RESEARCH** as
a gift for Mum this
Mother's Day. Visit
breastcancertrials.
org.au and get a
special Mother's
Day card for her.

7 SUNDAY

APRIL						
S	M	T	W	T	F	S
30						1
2	3	4	5	6	7	8
9	10	11	12	13	14	15
16	17	18	19	20	21	22
23	24	25	26	27	28	29

MAY						
S	M	T	W	T	F	S
	1	2	3	4	5	6
7	8	9	10	11	12	13
14	15	16	17	18	19	20
21	22	23	24	25	26	27
28	29	30	31			

JUNE						
S	M	T	W	T	F	S
				1	2	3
4	5	6	7	8	9	10
11	12	13	14	15	16	17
18	19	20	21	22	23	24
25	26	27	28	29	30	

8 MONDAY

9 TUESDAY

10 WEDNESDAY

11 THURSDAY

12 FRIDAY

13 SATURDAY

ALONG WITH YOUR GP, many pharmacies also offer free blood pressure checks and blood glucose tests. Visit findapharmacy.com.au to book an appointment.

14 SUNDAY MOTHER'S DAY

		APRIL				
S	M	T	W	T	F	S
30						1
2	3	4	5	6	7	8
9	10	11	12	13	14	15
16	17	18	19	20	21	22
23	24	25	26	27	28	29

		MAY				
S	M	T	W	T	F	S
	1	2	3	4	5	6
7	8	9	10	11	12	13
14	15	16	17	18	19	20
21	22	23	24	25	26	27
28	29	30	31			

		JUNE				
S	M	T	W	T	F	S
				1	2	3
4	5	6	7	8	9	10
11	12	13	14	15	16	17
18	19	20	21	22	23	24
25	26	27	28	29	30	

15 MONDAY

16 TUESDAY

17 WEDNESDAY

18 THURSDAY

May
2023

19 FRIDAY

20 SATURDAY

> **USE HEALTHY COOKING METHODS** at home. Roasting, steaming, poaching, slow-cooking and stir-frying in a splash of oil are all ideal for heart health.

21 SUNDAY

APRIL

S	M	T	W	T	F	S
30						1
2	3	4	5	6	7	8
9	10	11	12	13	14	15
16	17	18	19	20	21	22
23	24	25	26	27	28	29

MAY

S	M	T	W	T	F	S
	1	2	3	4	5	6
7	8	9	10	11	12	13
14	15	16	17	18	19	20
21	22	23	24	25	26	27
28	29	30	31			

JUNE

S	M	T	W	T	F	S
				1	2	3
4	5	6	7	8	9	10
11	12	13	14	15	16	17
18	19	20	21	22	23	24
25	26	27	28	29	30	

22 MONDAY

23 TUESDAY

24 WEDNESDAY

25 THURSDAY

26 FRIDAY NATIONAL SORRY DAY

27 SATURDAY

> **SMOKING DAMAGES THE BLOOD VESSELS** and makes you four times more likely to die of heart attack or stroke. Call Quitline for help on 137 848.

28 SUNDAY

66

I'm participating in a clinical trial to see if breast cancer can be prevented in women like me who carry the BRCA1 gene mutation. It's scary to be told you could develop breast cancer. Being on the trial makes me feel like I have some control over my life.

Samantha Weeks,
age 27

let's talk about
YOUR FINANCES

Financial wellbeing can be harder for women to achieve than men, thanks in part to a lack of confidence and ongoing wage inequality. Strive towards financial security with active involvement in all money matters.

While saving for a rainy day and avoiding unnecessary purchases are two proven strategies for achieving financial health, there are times when spending money is also beneficial. Here are seven occasions when it's OK to spend big.

1 YOUR HEALTH
A healthy diet and regular exercise are known to help combat a number of health conditions and diseases. As such, spending money on medical care, therapy, exercise classes, gym equipment, health insurance or a fruit and veg delivery service could save you in medical bills in the long run.

2 PERSONAL FULFILMENT
It's OK to splash out on experiences, services and products that bring you joy or make life easier. For example, massages, theatre tickets or a house cleaner are all worthwhile expenses. Likewise, spending on your hobbies is a great form of self-care.

3 PEACE OF MIND
Protect your family and belongings with an appropriate level of insurance. This can include car, home and contents, pet, travel, health, life or income protection insurance. It will pay for itself should things go wrong.

4 QUALITY
When shopping for clothes, electronics or homewares, it can be tempting to buy the cheapest option. But if you need to replace this item frequently, it could end up costing more than a superior brand or model. The same rule applies to items that can improve your quality of life, like a supportive mattress, good walking shoes or prescriptive skincare.

5 ROMANCE
The average marriage lasts 12 years, with close to 50,000 divorces granted each year. Keep your relationship thriving with a dedicated 'romance fund', which can be used for fun dates or 'just because' gifts.

6 EDUCATION
Even with a degree, further study may lead to a promotion or pay rise. If you're retired, learning something new can prevent boredom and provide opportunities for socialisation. Look for online courses, workshops or seminars to help you upskill or to provide extra mental stimulation.

7 GIVING BACK
Donating to a cause that you believe in will make you feel good while making a difference. Not to mention, there are tax benefits to many charitable contributions.

What is financial abuse?

One in six Australian women will experience some form of financial abuse, regardless of age, sexuality, socioeconomic status, ethnicity or level of education. The abuser is often their partner, a family member, carer or friend. Financial abuse is a form of family violence, and occurs when one partner uses money to control or exploit their partner and limit their financial independence. Similarly, elder abuse occurs when a trusted person misuses their position or causes financial harm to an older person. Financial abuse can have an effect on a victim's physical and mental health and result in large amounts of debt being accrued against their name.

THE WARNING SIGNS OF FINANCIAL ABUSE

There are lots of ways someone can be financially abusive towards a loved one, many quite subtle. In some cases, it may be disguised as a display of affection – trying to help or take care of you. Here are some of the warning signs.

- Scrutinising or controlling how all of the household income is spent
- Restricting your access to money, bank accounts or benefits
- Making you ask permission to spend your own money
- Cancelling credit cards or hiding bills and financial statements
- Hiding assets from you
- Keeping financial secrets
- Withdrawing large amounts of money from your account
- Stealing from you
- Forcing you to claim government benefits
- Taking money out of your pension
- Selling your possessions without your permission
- Forcing you to change your will or appoint them as power of attorney
- Taking out loans, debts and/or credit cards in your name without your knowledge or permission
- Refusing to contribute to shared costs or child support
- Using your money without your knowledge or consent
- Forcing you to sign documents or forging your signature
- Stopping or forbidding you from working or studying
- Denying you access to the internet, phone or transport to sabotage work, study or employment opportunities
- Threatening or punishing you if you don't give them money.

A FINANCIAL ADVISER CAN ASSIST WITH...

Superannuation

Investing

Retirement

Saving

Budgeting

Debt management

Insurance

Estate planning

Tax management

Do I need a financial adviser?

Some financial matters are more complex than others, and you may wish to seek guidance from a qualified professional. A good financial planner or adviser can assess your situation and create a tailored strategy to meet your goals, such as planning for retirement, selecting insurance cover, budgeting for the kids' education or investing. You'll pay for the service, but ultimately this targeted advice could save you time, effort and money.

If this is something you'd like to explore, take your time choosing the right adviser for your needs. Your super fund or financial institution may be able to recommend someone, or ask friends and family for suggestions. Most advisers don't charge for the first consultation, so meet with a few to compare their fees and services. Ask lots of questions and make sure you feel comfortable entrusting your personal information with them.

Anyone providing financial advice is required to be listed on the Financial Advisers Register on the ASIC website (asic.gov.au). To be listed, they must also meet a certain standard of education and experience and adhere to a code of ethics.

Money lessons for kids

It's never too early – or too late – to have conversations about money with your children, especially now that we live in an almost cashless state. Look for the following opportunities to demonstrate the value of money, and set them on the path to financial independence.

CHILDREN AGED 2-5	CHILDREN AGED 5-10
• Start the money conversations early using daily examples. For example, when you're getting ready for work in the morning, chat about your job and how you earn money. • Teach the concept of paying for a service or product by letting children give the money to the cashier to purchase groceries. • Play shop using real notes and coins to show them what money looks like and explain the different values. • Teach them delayed gratification. If your child sees something they like in the shops, show them the item's price tag and suggest they ask for it for Christmas or their birthday.	• From this age, you may like to give pocket money for completing tasks or chores. For instance, washing the car, folding washing or stacking the dishwasher. If tasks aren't completed, they don't earn their money. • Explain the concept of ATMs. They're not just a machine that spits out unlimited money; you're accessing your own savings. • Give them a shopping catalogue and an imaginary budget and set them the task of shopping for a family meal or an event like a birthday party while staying within budget. • Open a kids savings account in their name to teach the value of making regular deposits.
CHILDREN AGED 11-15	CHILDREN AGED 16-21
• Involve them in some purchasing decisions, such as selecting a new pair of soccer boots or a birthday present for a friend. Explain the concept of quality over quantity; the cheapest purchases aren't always the best. • When they turn 15, help them find their first casual job. Teach them how to read a payslip and encourage them to save a portion of their wages and donate some to charity. • They may want to buy something for themselves, such as concert tickets, new clothes or a game console. Help them work out if it's a need or want and make a plan for how they will save up to pay for it.	• Get them involved in doing the family budget. Explain how much money you have each week and how it's spent. • Ask for their help shopping around for the best deal on big purchases, like an appliance, new car or holiday flights. • Begin conversations about future goals (study, travel, a new car, moving out of home) and how they might achieve them. • Talk about credit and debt. There may be times when they need to pay for something that they don't have money for. Where will the money come from and how will they pay it back? Will there be interest to pay as well?

ADULT CHILDREN

As children become financially dependent, you may continue to provide some financial support, such as contributing towards a house deposit, being a guarantor on their home loan or helping with childcare. Alternatively, you might need to ask them for financial help. Have lots of open conversations about the support that you or they can give, seek independent advice and set boundaries from the start.

WE NEED YOUR FEEDBACK

Help us to keep in touch with what matters to you and ensure your diary remains relevant, practical and informative by completing our short online survey today.

You can also unlock special offers like pre-ordering your 2024 Australian Women's Health Diary at a discounted price!

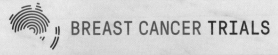

BREAST CANCER **TRIALS**

The Australian Women's Health Diary is an initiative of Breast Cancer Trials produced in conjunction with our friends at The Australian Women's Weekly. For 25 years, not only has this diary helped Australian women to be organised and informed about their health, it has also saved lives from breast cancer.

Learn more at breastcancertrials.org.au or call 1800 423 444.

MAY						
S	M	T	W	T	F	S
	1	2	3	4	5	6
7	8	9	10	11	12	13
14	15	16	17	18	19	20
21	22	23	24	25	26	27
28	29	30	31			

JUNE						
S	M	T	W	T	F	S
				1	2	3
4	5	6	7	8	9	10
11	12	13	14	15	16	17
18	19	20	21	22	23	24
25	26	27	28	29	30	

JULY						
S	M	T	W	T	F	S
30	31					1
2	3	4	5	6	7	8
9	10	11	12	13	14	15
16	17	18	19	20	21	22
23	24	25	26	27	28	29

29 MONDAY RECONCILIATION DAY (ACT)

30 TUESDAY

31 WEDNESDAY

1 THURSDAY

June
2023

2 FRIDAY

3 SATURDAY

4 SUNDAY

	MAY								JUNE								JULY					
S	M	T	W	T	F	S		S	M	T	W	T	F	S		S	M	T	W	T	F	S
	1	2	3	4	5	6					1	2	3		30	31					1
7	8	9	10	11	12	13		4	5	6	7	8	9	10		2	3	4	5	6	7	8
14	15	16	17	18	19	20		11	12	13	14	15	16	17		9	10	11	12	13	14	15
21	22	23	24	25	26	27		18	19	20	21	22	23	24		16	17	18	19	20	21	22
28	29	30	31					25	26	27	28	29	30			23	24	25	26	27	28	29

5 MONDAY WESTERN AUSTRALIA DAY (WA)

6 TUESDAY

7 WEDNESDAY

8 THURSDAY

9 FRIDAY

10 SATURDAY

> **SAVE MONEY** by programming your washer, dryer or washing machine to begin its cycle during off-peak periods (usually late at night or early morning).

11 SUNDAY

MAY

S	M	T	W	T	F	S
	1	2	3	4	5	6
7	8	9	10	11	12	13
14	15	16	17	18	19	20
21	22	23	24	25	26	27
28	29	30	31			

JUNE

S	M	T	W	T	F	S
				1	2	3
4	5	6	7	8	9	10
11	12	13	14	15	16	17
18	19	20	21	22	23	24
25	26	27	28	29	30	

JULY

S	M	T	W	T	F	S
30	31					1
2	3	4	5	6	7	8
9	10	11	12	13	14	15
16	17	18	19	20	21	22
23	24	25	26	27	28	29

12 MONDAY QUEEN'S BIRTHDAY (ACT, NSW, NT, SA, TAS, VIC)

13 TUESDAY

14 WEDNESDAY

15 THURSDAY

16 FRIDAY

17 SATURDAY

MAKE A DONATION to breast cancer research before June 30 to claim it as a deduction in your tax return. Call 1800 423 444 or visit breastcancer trials.org.au.

18 SUNDAY

	MAY							JUNE							JULY					
S	M	T	W	T	F	S	S	M	T	W	T	F	S	S	M	T	W	T	F	S
	1	2	3	4	5	6					1	2	3	30	31					1
7	8	9	10	11	12	13	4	5	6	7	8	9	10	2	3	4	5	6	7	8
14	15	16	17	18	19	20	11	12	13	14	15	16	17	9	10	11	12	13	14	15
21	22	23	24	25	26	27	18	19	20	21	22	23	24	16	17	18	19	20	21	22
28	29	30	31				25	26	27	28	29	30		23	24	25	26	27	28	29

19 MONDAY

20 TUESDAY

21 WEDNESDAY

22 THURSDAY

23 FRIDAY

24 SATURDAY

STAY ON TOP OF CREDIT CARD DEBT by paying the balance on time. Set up an automatic transfer each month, timed around payday so you'll have the funds to cover it.

25 SUNDAY

		MAY							JUNE							JULY				
S	M	T	W	T	F	S	S	M	T	W	T	F	S	S	M	T	W	T	F	S
	1	2	3	4	5	6					1	2	3	30	31					1
7	8	9	10	11	12	13	4	5	6	7	8	9	10	2	3	4	5	6	7	8
14	15	16	17	18	19	20	11	12	13	14	15	16	17	9	10	11	12	13	14	15
21	22	23	24	25	26	27	18	19	20	21	22	23	24	16	17	18	19	20	21	22
28	29	30	31				25	26	27	28	29	30		23	24	25	26	27	28	29

26 MONDAY

27 TUESDAY

28 WEDNESDAY

29 THURSDAY   EID AL-ADHA (ISLAMIC HOLIDAY)

30 FRIDAY

1 SATURDAY

> **IF YOU HAVE MULTIPLE DEBTS,** consider rolling them all into one personal loan with a single interest rate and one set of recurring payments.

2 SUNDAY FIRST DAY OF NAIDOC WEEK

> I was first diagnosed 12 years ago, one year after my daughter had breast cancer. I now have metastatic breast cancer. There is no cure, but hopefully treatments can keep it under control. I try not to dwell on it, and instead appreciate the time I have with family and friends.

Mary Egerton, first diagnosed at age 70

let's talk about
AGEING

Making healthy lifestyle choices now can put you in good health for your later years. That means eating well, staying physically, mentally and socially active and prioritising a good night's sleep.

I t can be difficult as a parent when grown children leave home. You may experience sadness, loss of purpose, loneliness and anxiety. This common phenomenon, known as empty nest syndrome, is more prevalent in women, particularly those who've been the main caregiver. Help fill the void by putting these coping strategies in place.

1 ACKNOWLEDGE YOUR FEELINGS
Give yourself time to adapt to this change. Seek advice and support from your partner or friends who may be in the same situation. If you feel depressed, speak to your doctor or a counsellor.

2 SHIFT THE FOCUS TO YOU
If your parenting years were spent putting your children's needs first, now's the time to prioritise your own interests. Make a list of things you've always wanted to do, such as books to read, restaurants to try and travel destinations to visit.

3 RECONNECT WITH OTHERS
With all your time and energy focused on the kids, sometimes relationships fall by the wayside. Reconnect with your partner or friends by going for walks, cooking together or just enjoying an uninterrupted conversation. Show affection and appreciation as you rediscover common ground that doesn't involve the kids.

4 LEARN SOMETHING NEW
Picking up a new hobby or taking a course in something that interests you will reduce stress and challenge your brain. Local community groups and colleges have plenty of options. Sign up individually or with your partner – having separate and shared interests will give you more to talk about when the house feels quiet.

5 SPEND TIME VOLUNTEERING
Giving back to the community can teach you new skills and give you renewed sense of purpose. Try animal shelters, community gardens, hospitals, homeless services, sports clubs or bushcare programs – start with an hour and see where it takes you.

6 REINVENT FAMILY TIME
While your children may be out of home, they're not out of your life. Organise weekly or fortnightly meals and outings to catch up on each other's news. Watching them build their new lives, while supporting them from afar, can be a wonderful next chapter.

For more information, visit Relationships Australia; relationships.org.au

The signs of hearing loss

From work and socialising to building relationships, good hearing keeps you connected to the people you love and the things you like to do. But our hearing can deteriorate as we get older. Over half the population aged 60-70 will have some form of hearing loss, and this increases to 70 per cent after age 70 and 80 per cent after 80. While in most cases hearing loss can't be reversed, there are options to improve it or prevent it from getting worse, such as hearing aids, cochlear implants, surgery and even phone apps that amplify sounds for you. If you have any of these symptoms of hearing loss, see your doctor or make an appointment with an audiologist.

For more information, visit Hearing Australia; hearing.com.au

Having trouble hearing in noisy places like restaurants or shopping centres

———

Having difficulty understanding or following conversations

———

Asking people to repeat themselves often

———

Hearing sounds as muffled or spoken words as mumbled

———

Having the TV volume up so loud that others complain or comment

———

Missing everyday sounds like the oven timer, your phone ringing or a knock on the door

———

Buzzing or ringing in your ears

———

Finding that loud noises cause you more discomfort than previously.

Boost your brain power

Do you find yourself forgetting where you left your car keys? Or struggling to recall a familiar name? Memory lapses can occur as you get older, but in many cases they can be reversed. Just as our muscles lose tone and strength if they're not in use, so does the brain. Stay sharp and alert with these brain-boosting strategies.

CHALLENGE YOUR BRAIN Mental exercises like reading, trivia and 'thinking' activities like crosswords, Sudoku, chess, cards and Wordle are great for boosting mental capacity. Likewise, learning a new language or instrument, knitting, painting or tackling some DIY projects around the house can have the same effect.

EXERCISE EVERY DAY Doing some form of moderate movement each day can help improve memory, reasoning abilities and reaction times – aim for at least 30 minutes. Tai Chi, yoga and dance, where you have to memorise or follow set movements, are three great options.

EAT A HEALTHY DIET Good nutrition will keep your brain firing on all cylinders. Omega-3 fatty acids are essential for learning and memory, and can help slow age-related mental decline and ward off Alzheimer's disease. You'll find them in oily fish, walnuts, chia seeds, tofu, leafy greens and vegetable oils like canola and soybean.

KEEP UP YOUR SOCIAL LIFE Catching up with friends, attending networking events, volunteering or taking a class may help ward off dementia. You'll stimulate and exercise the brain by engaging in conversation, recalling events, recognising faces and reading body language.

Fibre-rich meal ideas for a healthy gut

Poor fibre intake can lead to constipation at any age, but as we get older, reduced physical activity, inadequate fluid intake, poor food choices and some medications can exacerbate the problem. The simplest solution is to consume 25-30g of fibre per day and drink more water. You'll find fibre in fruits, vegetables and legumes, along with wholegrain breads and cereals, nuts and seeds. Eat from a variety of plant-based sources with these fibre-packed options.

BREAKFAST

Top porridge with sliced pear (skin on) and ¼ cup chopped dates or prunes (soaked overnight). Sprinkle a little cinnamon or nuts on top.

Toast 1-2 slices wholegrain bread and top with half an avocado. Scatter over some chia seeds or flax seeds for added crunch.

Add 1 cup baby spinach or kale to a berry smoothie, or some frozen cauliflower, avocado or a spoonful of nut butter to a banana smoothie.

LUNCH

Make a salad of canned baby beetroot, rocket, canned lentils (drained) and crumbled fetta. Dress with extra virgin olive oil and balsamic vinegar.

Try a frittata. Whisk 6 eggs and add 3 cups cooked vegies and ¾ cup grated cheese. Bake in an oven dish at 180°C for 35-40 minutes. Serves 4.

Roast a sweet potato (skin left on), halve and top with a bean and corn salsa. Sprinkle goat's cheese, parmesan or grated cheddar over the top.

DINNER

Dish up chilli con carne made from beef mince, grated carrot, red kidney beans, diced tomatoes and taco seasoning. Serve with brown rice.

Make a big pot of vegetable curry (try pumpkin, eggplant, cauliflower, chickpeas or any other vegies on hand). Serve with wholemeal flatbread.

Nothing beats a simple stir-fry. Try salmon or chicken with carrot (skin on), broccoli and peas, served with brown rice or buckwheat noodles.

For more information, visit Nutrition Australia; nutritionaustralia.org

How ageing affects our sleep

It's common to experience a shift in sleeping patterns as we get older. You may wake earlier, feel tired during the day, have trouble falling asleep or wake often during the night. Some sleep problems also become more prevalent with age. For instance, at least one in four older Australians have sleep apnoea or periodic limb movement disorder, while four in 10 suffer from insomnia.

The causes of your sleeping difficulties can be varied. For starters, from middle age, our bodies begin to produce less melatonin, the hormone that promotes sleep. Stress, menopausal hot flushes, a loss of bladder control, a lack of physical activity and some age-related medical conditions and their medications can also play a part. Taking long naps during the day can make it harder to sleep at night, too.

So how can you improve your sleep? The most important thing is to maintain regular sleep habits to strengthen your body's sleep-wake rhythm. Try to go to bed at the same time each night (not too early) and wake at the same time each morning. Avoid sleeping in, even if you've had a broken night's sleep. Exercise or plan stimulating activities during the day to tire yourself out, and if you're going to nap, limit it to 20 minutes, preferably by mid-afternoon.

If lack of sleep begins to affect your mood or you're feeling excessively sleepy during the day, speak to your GP who may prescribe melatonin or refer you to a sleep specialist.

For more information, visit the Sleep Health Foundation; sleephealthfoundation.org.au

JUNE						
S	M	T	W	T	F	S
				1	2	3
4	5	6	7	8	9	10
11	12	13	14	15	16	17
18	19	20	21	22	23	24
25	26	27	28	29	30	

JULY						
S	M	T	W	T	F	S
30	31					1
2	3	4	5	6	7	8
9	10	11	12	13	14	15
16	17	18	19	20	21	22
23	24	25	26	27	28	29

AUGUST						
S	M	T	W	T	F	S
		1	2	3	4	5
6	7	8	9	10	11	12
13	14	15	16	17	18	19
20	21	22	23	24	25	26
27	28	29	30	31		

3 MONDAY

4 TUESDAY

5 WEDNESDAY

6 THURSDAY

July
2023

7 FRIDAY

8 SATURDAY

> **EAT YOUR FRUIT AND VEG WHOLE,** not as a juice. The juicing process breaks down up to 90 per cent of the beneficial fibre found in the pectin and the skin.

9 SUNDAY

		JUNE				
S	M	T	W	T	F	S
				1	2	3
4	5	6	7	8	9	10
11	12	13	14	15	16	17
18	19	20	21	22	23	24
25	26	27	28	29	30	

		JULY				
S	M	T	W	T	F	S
30	31					1
2	3	4	5	6	7	8
9	10	11	12	13	14	15
16	17	18	19	20	21	22
23	24	25	26	27	28	29

		AUGUST				
S	M	T	W	T	F	S
		1	2	3	4	5
6	7	8	9	10	11	12
13	14	15	16	17	18	19
20	21	22	23	24	25	26
27	28	29	30	31		

10 MONDAY

11 TUESDAY

12 WEDNESDAY

13 THURSDAY

July
2023

14 FRIDAY   BASTILLE DAY (FRANCE)

15 SATURDAY

> **KEEP UP YOUR DENTAL VISITS** if you're having difficulty with your teeth, gums or dentures to ensure you can continue to enjoy a variety of foods without restriction.

16 SUNDAY

		J U N E				
S	M	T	W	T	F	S
				1	2	3
4	5	6	7	8	9	10
11	12	13	14	15	16	17
18	19	20	21	22	23	24
25	26	27	28	29	30	

		J U L Y				
S	M	T	W	T	F	S
30	31					1
2	3	4	5	6	7	8
9	10	11	12	13	14	15
16	17	18	19	20	21	22
23	24	25	26	27	28	29

		A U G U S T				
S	M	T	W	T	F	S
		1	2	3	4	5
6	7	8	9	10	11	12
13	14	15	16	17	18	19
20	21	22	23	24	25	26
27	28	29	30	31		

17 MONDAY

18 TUESDAY

19 WEDNESDAY MUHARRAM/ISLAMIC NEW YEAR

20 THURSDAY

21 FRIDAY

22 SATURDAY

SNORING CAN AFFECT YOUR SLEEP and your partner's. Seek medical treatment for the snoring, or try using a white noise app or wearing earplugs to drown out the sound at night.

23 SUNDAY

		JUNE							JULY							AUGUST				
S	M	T	W	T	F	S	S	M	T	W	T	F	S	S	M	T	W	T	F	S
				1	2	3	30	31					1			1	2	3	4	5
4	5	6	7	8	9	10	2	3	4	5	6	7	8	6	7	8	9	10	11	12
11	12	13	14	15	16	17	9	10	11	12	13	14	15	13	14	15	16	17	18	19
18	19	20	21	22	23	24	16	17	18	19	20	21	22	20	21	22	23	24	25	26
25	26	27	28	29	30		23	24	25	26	27	28	29	27	28	29	30	31		

24 MONDAY

25 TUESDAY

26 WEDNESDAY

27 THURSDAY

28 FRIDAY

29 SATURDAY

> **IF MOBILITY IS IMPAIRED** or limited, you can stay physically active with chair-based exercises, assisted walking and standing or hydrotherapy.

30 SUNDAY

WHY I SUPPORT BREAST CANCER TRIALS

I may have passed the BRCA1 gene mutation to my children. I never want my daughter Taya to go through breast cancer like I have, or make the choices I've had to make and remove her breasts and ovaries to reduce her risk. I hope Taya's future will be different.

Rebecca Matthews, diagnosed at age 29, pictured with her family

let's talk about
FAMILY

Families come in all shapes and sizes, each with their own unique needs and challenges. Start by laying the foundations for a healthy and supportive home environment using the tips in this chapter.

Regardless of what form your family takes – nuclear, blended, single-parent, foster, rainbow – having special traditions or rituals is the perfect way to celebrate this unique bond. Family rituals provide children with predictability and a sense of security and safety. They're especially important during times of crisis or big change, to help maintain a sense of normalcy. Some traditions are passed on from one generation to the next. With a focus on being present in the moment, family rituals usually revolve around sharing something special together and building memories. They don't need to be big or complicated. Here are just a few ideas.

CREATE YOUR OWN FAMILY RITUALS
- Eat dinner together and talk about your day
- At bedtime, take turns saying something you're grateful for or looking forward to
- Create rituals that revolve around special occasions. For example, home-made cards for birthdays, sparklers for New Year, decorating the house for Ramadan or a special outing for Mother's Day
- Cheer for your favourite sporting team as a family – live or on TV
- Enjoy weekly activities like movie nights, dance parties, games nights or picnics
- Plan a regular meal that everyone helps prepare, be it Taco Tuesdays, Homemade Pizza Night or Pancake Sundays
- Enjoy one-on-one outings, such as bowling with Dad or a pamper day with Mum
- Go camping or have holidays at the same destination each year.

WHEN FAMILY TRADITIONS END
As children get older or circumstances change, your rituals may need to evolve. For example, when teenagers get a casual job and are no longer available for Sunday bike rides. Death, marriage, divorce or a move may also alter the way special occasions can be celebrated.

Changing the tradition could be as simple as choosing a different day or a different activity, but sometimes you'll need to let go of the old ways and think of a new ritual that has meaning for all involved. Seek input from everyone to find a new common interest or reallocate roles that were traditionally held by someone else. Start the discussions early to give people time to emotionally adjust to the new plan, and make sure everyone's thoughts and ideas are heard. Remain flexible – sometimes a new ritual will need to be trialled or tweaked a few times before you find one that works for your family.

For more information, visit Raising Children Network; raisingchildren.net.au

Health checks for children

Stay on top of your family's health needs by noting the following check-ups and reminders in your diary. Recommendations may vary from state to state, so always seek advice from your GP or family health care clinic if you're unsure.

INFANTS (0-12 mths)

☐ Soon after birth your baby will be given a head-to-toe medical assessment to check their head size and shape, eyes, hearing, mouth, heart, lungs, hands, feet, spine, hips, reflexes and genitals.

Your family GP, paediatrician or family health nurse will continue to monitor your baby's development at ☐ 1-4 weeks, ☐ 6-8 weeks, ☐ 4 months, ☐ 6 months and ☐ 12 months, or more often if needed.

☐ You'll receive an infant health record book, which can be used to track your baby's height, weight, head circumference and other developmental aspects.

Routine, funded vaccinations are recommended as follows:

☐ **At birth** – vitamin K and hepatitis B

☐ **2 months** – diphtheria, tetanus, whooping cough, hepatitis B, polio, haemophilus influenzae type b, rotavirus, pneumococcal

☐ **4 months** – as above

☐ **6 months** – as above, minus rotavirus

☐ **12 months** – measles, mumps, rubella, meningococcal ACWY, pneumococcal

☐ A yearly influenza immunisation is recommended and funded by the government for children from 6 months until 5 years of age.

TODDLERS & PRESCHOOLERS (1-5 yrs)

Health checks continue at ☐ 18 months, ☐ 2 years, ☐ 3 years and ☐ 4 years.

☐ Annual dental health check-ups can begin from age 1. This allows the dentist to spot any concerns early, while helping take the fear out of the experience for children.

Routine, funded vaccinations are recommended as follows:

☐ **18 months** – diphtheria, tetanus, mumps, rubella, chickenpox, whooping cough, measles, and haemophilus influenzae type b

☐ **4 years** – diphtheria, tetanus, whooping cough and polio

☐ Continue with your free influenza immunisations until five years of age.

Prior to starting school, it's recommended that all children have a ☐ vision, ☐ hearing and ☐ dental check-up to identify any issues that may affect their learning experience.

PRIMARY CHILDREN (5-12 yrs)

See your GP for regular check-ups and advice on common concerns at this age, such as coughs, colds and infections, diarrhoea and vomiting, allergies, asthma, rashes, fever, head lice and worms.

Continue 6-12 monthly dental check-ups. Most children begin to lose their baby teeth around age 6, and should have all adult teeth except wisdom teeth by age 12.

Influenza immunisations are recommended but are no longer government funded.

TEENAGERS (12-18 yrs)

Teenage girls should have five-yearly Cervical Screening Tests once sexually active. Regular STI tests for sexually active boys and girls are also recommended.

Annual dental check-ups should continue. Wisdom teeth usually come through in the late teens or early 20s. If problems occur, your dentist may recommend removal.

Routine, funded vaccinations are recommended as follows:

☐ **12-13 years** – booster for diphtheria, tetanus and whooping cough, as well as two human papillomavirus (HPV) immunisations (boys and girls)

☐ **14-16 years** – booster against the A, C, W and Y strains of meningococcal disease

Vaping in young people

While smoking cigarettes looks to have lost its appeal with most Australian teenagers, the popularity of vaping continues to grow. E-cigarettes or 'vapes' are battery-powered devices that hold cartridges of nicotine or non-nicotine liquids. These liquids also contain artificial flavourings and various other chemicals. The liquid is heated into a vapour and inhaled into the lungs. Despite the need for a doctor's prescription to purchase e-cigarettes containing nicotine, 11 per cent of Australians aged 14 and over admit to having tried vaping at least once. Marketed as a less harmful alternative to cigarettes, the long-term health effects of e-cigarettes are yet to be determined. Early studies suggest vaping can harm adolescent brain development and lead to tobacco use and dependence later in life. So what, as a parent, can you do to inform your kids about the risks of vaping?

1 Lead by example and don't use e-cigarettes, especially around children.

2 Equip yourself with accurate and current information about vaping and have an open discussion about the risks with your teen. Focus on how you care about them and want them to be healthy. Be honest; avoid exaggerated statements.

3 Time your conversations for when you're both calm and not distracted – for instance, while driving or sharing a meal.

4 Stay calm and never assume or judge. If you suspect your teen is vaping, avoid searching their belongings as this could undermine trust. Instead, reassure them that they can always talk to you.

For more information, visit the Alcohol and Drug Foundation; adf.org.au

WHAT IS BULLYING?
Bullying is an ongoing misuse of power in a relationship, with the intention of causing physical and/or psychological harm.

How to support kids when they're being bullied

One in four Australian students experience bullying at some stage. Bullying can have a negative impact on a child's appetite, concentration, self-esteem, confidence, sleep and physical wellbeing, and may lead to feelings of fear, anger, loneliness and hopelessness and, in extreme cases, thoughts of self-harm or suicide.

WHAT DOES BULLYING LOOK LIKE

Bullying can take the following forms:
Verbal Name-calling, teasing, intimidation, homophobic, sexist or racist remarks.
Physical Pushing, kicking, spitting, tripping, hitting, damaging personal belongings.
Social Lying, spreading rumours, practical jokes, excluding or embarrassing someone.
Cyber Using technology or software to abuse, attack or intimidate someone with hurtful messages, comments or pictures.

WHAT SHOULD YOU DO IF YOUR CHILD IS BEING BULLIED?

At home: Encourage them to open up to you and tell you the whole story. Listen calmly and without interruption. Reassure them that they've done the right thing in speaking up. Ask what they would like to happen from here – they may just want the bullying to end rather than seeing the perpetrator punished.

Outside of home: If the bullying occurred at school, it's important to let the school know. Make an appointment with your child's teacher or school principal and take along notes from your conversations or any supporting screenshots, text messages or similar. Ask about the school's bullying policy and what can be done to ensure your child's safety, and arrange a follow-up appointment for a future date.

For more information, visit the National Centre Against Bullying; ncab.org.au

The important role of grandparents

Grandparents can bring incredible value to a child's upbringing, teaching them life skills and providing a greater sense of belonging. In an ideal world, we would live close to our families and play an active role in each other's lives, however not every family has grandparents to turn to. Thankfully, others can fill the role of a 'grandfriend' – think aunts, uncles, neighbours, older colleagues or friends. Here are some of the benefits you might gain from these relationships.

THE PERKS OF HAVING A GRANDPARENT
- Grandparents have a wealth of life experience and can share valuable life lessons. They can also pass on family traditions and share cultural knowledge.
- Their memories, stories and photos of a child's parents and relatives can help provide a child with a sense of belonging.
- Grandparents can provide emotional support to both the grandchild and their parents, stepping in to care for the kids when the adult children need a break.
- They provide a different type of care to that of parents; an extra layer of protection and comfort for a more holistic upbringing.
- Children have another 'safe' adult who they can turn to for advice or support.
- Grandparents teach children different perspectives and ways of doing things, and expose them to new interests.
- Children learn how to interact with adults of different ages and backgrounds.

THE JOYS OF BEING A GRANDPARENT
- Grandkids keep their grandparents on the go and have been shown to help boost mood and give a greater sense of purpose.
- Caring for grandchildren can help combat feelings of loneliness.

- Grandkids can teach their grandparents new tricks, from telling you about their favourite TV show or explaining the rules of a video game to showing you how to use features on your smart phone.
- The arrival of a grandchild can provide a chance to mend a strained relationship with your adult child or their partner, or to form stronger bonds.

	JULY					
S	M	T	W	T	F	S
30	31					1
2	3	4	5	6	7	8
9	10	11	12	13	14	15
16	17	18	19	20	21	22
23	24	25	26	27	28	29

	AUGUST					
S	M	T	W	T	F	S
		1	2	3	4	5
6	7	8	9	10	11	12
13	14	15	16	17	18	19
20	21	22	23	24	25	26
27	28	29	30	31		

	SEPTEMBER					
S	M	T	W	T	F	S
					1	2
3	4	5	6	7	8	9
10	11	12	13	14	15	16
17	18	19	20	21	22	23
24	25	26	27	28	29	30

31 MONDAY

1 TUESDAY

2 WEDNESDAY

3 THURSDAY

August
2023

4 FRIDAY

5 SATURDAY

EAT AS A FAMILY
to promote healthy
eating habits, high
self-esteem and
lower levels of
stress. Everyone
should have a task:
cooking, setting the
table or cleaning
up afterwards.

6 SUNDAY

		JULY				
S	M	T	W	T	F	S
30	31					1
2	3	4	5	6	7	8
9	10	11	12	13	14	15
16	17	18	19	20	21	22
23	24	25	26	27	28	29

		AUGUST				
S	M	T	W	T	F	S
		1	2	3	4	5
6	7	8	9	10	11	12
13	14	15	16	17	18	19
20	21	22	23	24	25	26
27	28	29	30	31		

		SEPTEMBER				
S	M	T	W	T	F	S
					1	2
3	4	5	6	7	8	9
10	11	12	13	14	15	16
17	18	19	20	21	22	23
24	25	26	27	28	29	30

7 MONDAY BANK HOLIDAY (NSW), PICNIC DAY (NT)

8 TUESDAY

9 WEDNESDAY

10 THURSDAY

11 FRIDAY

12 SATURDAY

TEENAGERS CAN BE SUSCEPTIBLE to mental health concerns. Seek professional help if you notice uncharacteristic behaviours or actions that last for more than a few weeks.

13 SUNDAY

JULY						
S	M	T	W	T	F	S
30	31					1
2	3	4	5	6	7	8
9	10	11	12	13	14	15
16	17	18	19	20	21	22
23	24	25	26	27	28	29

AUGUST						
S	M	T	W	T	F	S
		1	2	3	4	5
6	7	8	9	10	11	12
13	14	15	16	17	18	19
20	21	22	23	24	25	26
27	28	29	30	31		

SEPTEMBER						
S	M	T	W	T	F	S
					1	2
3	4	5	6	7	8	9
10	11	12	13	14	15	16
17	18	19	20	21	22	23
24	25	26	27	28	29	30

14 MONDAY

15 TUESDAY

16 WEDNESDAY

17 THURSDAY

August 2023

18 FRIDAY

19 SATURDAY

20 SUNDAY

	JULY					
S	M	T	W	T	F	S
30	31					1
2	3	4	5	6	7	8
9	10	11	12	13	14	15
16	17	18	19	20	21	22
23	24	25	26	27	28	29

	AUGUST					
S	M	T	W	T	F	S
		1	2	3	4	5
6	7	8	9	10	11	12
13	14	15	16	17	18	19
20	21	22	23	24	25	26
27	28	29	30	31		

	SEPTEMBER					
S	M	T	W	T	F	S
					1	2
3	4	5	6	7	8	9
10	11	12	13	14	15	16
17	18	19	20	21	22	23
24	25	26	27	28	29	30

21 MONDAY

22 TUESDAY

23 WEDNESDAY

24 THURSDAY

August
2023

25 FRIDAY

26 SATURDAY

27 SUNDAY

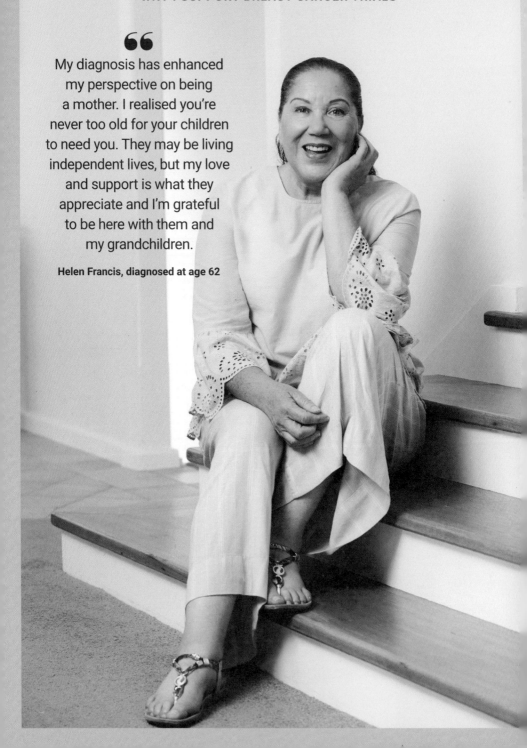

> 66
>
> My diagnosis has enhanced my perspective on being a mother. I realised you're never too old for your children to need you. They may be living independent lives, but my love and support is what they appreciate and I'm grateful to be here with them and my grandchildren.

Helen Francis, diagnosed at age 62

let's talk about
WELLBEING

Just as you take a proactive approach to healthy eating and exercise, so too should you find a routine and lifestyle that supports your mental wellbeing and helps you cope with whatever challenges come your way.

Stress is a common factor in many women's lives. In small doses, it can help boost productivity, energy levels and alertness. However, when we go through periods of prolonged or overwhelming stress, it can have negative consequences for our mind and body. This state of chronic stress is called burnout, with 30 per cent of women admitting to burning the candle at both ends in their personal and/or work lives.

WHAT IS BURNOUT?

Burnout is a state of complete mental, physical and emotional exhaustion. At its peak, you may feel like the life has been sucked right out of you. Burnout encompasses a wide range of symptoms, from physical to emotional. You may lack energy or motivation, feel detached or alone in the world, experience disrupted sleep and exhaustion or suffer from headaches, stomach aches, ulcers, frequent illness and lack of appetite. Many sufferers find it difficult to engage in activities they'd normally enjoy, or that they no longer care about things that once mattered to them. Emotional outbursts, irritation and increased reliance on drugs or alcohol to cope are also warning signs.

WHAT CAUSES BURNOUT?

Work-related stress is one of the main contributors – for example, working in a high-pressure environment, having an unrealistic workload or feeling undervalued. Lifestyle factors can also play a part – perhaps you lack time for relaxation or socialising, take care of young children with little time for yourself, don't have a good support network or aren't getting enough sleep. Then there are personality traits like being a perfectionist or high-achiever or always needing to be in control.

WAYS TO COMBAT BURNOUT

To reduce the impact of burnout and its symptoms, try the following:
- Turn to friends, colleagues or community groups for support
- Make time for daily exercise to boost your mood and energy levels
- Support your body with healthy meals and six to eight hours of sleep each night
- Find hobbies and interests outside of your work or home life
- Take regular time out to relax
- Learn to say no to tasks that you don't enjoy or are outside of your job description
- Re-evaluate your goals and priorities to enjoy a happier, stress-free existence.

For more information, visit Black Dog Institute; blackdoginstitute.org.au

How to shift that negative mindset

Many women may identify with a common psychological phenomenon known as negativity bias. Essentially it involves giving more weight to the negatives in a situation than the positives. For instance, taking criticism to heart while brushing off compliments, or being so busy wishing for all the things you don't have that you forget to appreciate the things you do. It becomes problematic when this negative outlook leads to social anxiety, depression, stress and low self-esteem.

HERE ARE SOME TRICKS TO TRAIN YOUR BRAIN TO SEE THE BRIGHT SIDE OF LIFE

Look for the silver lining. If your plans get cancelled, think of another activity you can enjoy with your free time. If it starts raining, tick watering the garden off your to-do list.

Practise gratitude. Make a list of five things, people or moments that brought you joy today. And express your gratitude to those around you – the bus driver, the mailman, your family or colleagues.

Spend time with positive people. Do you have a friend or family member who never fails to make you laugh and feel good about yourself? Seek them out when you're feeling down.

Create positive rituals. Start the day with some yoga stretches, listen to an uplifting podcast while cooking dinner, enjoy your cup of tea in the sunshine or do one nice thing for someone each day.

Help others. Interacting with those less fortunate can shift the focus away from your own worries and boost your mood.

Make plans. If you feel like there's nothing good happening in your life, plan something to look forward to. Perhaps dinner with a friend, a holiday or a new project to get stuck into.

3 ways to incorporate mindfulness into your day

Do you find yourself constantly operating on autopilot and not paying attention to what's going on around you? Or being so eaten up with worry that you can't sleep at night? One of the best ways to manage this endless stream of consciousness and mindless activity is to practise the ancient art of mindfulness. As well as reducing stress and improving mood, mindfulness is thought to help sharpen concentration, boost immune function and even fight obesity.

Mindfulness involves paying full attention to the thoughts and sensations you experience inside and outside your body within a particular moment. Unlike meditation, the aim isn't to clear your mind of all thought, but simply to observe these thoughts, along with your emotions and the five sensations of touch, taste, smell, sight and sound, without judgement. With practice, you can use mindfulness to focus your attention where you choose, worrying less about the past or future, disengaging from mental 'clutter' and simply enjoying what's happening in the here and now. Try these ideas.

1 **GET READY MINDFULLY.** Choose an activity that you do every day, such as brushing your teeth, driving to work or having a shower, and focus on the steps and sensations that come with it. The sound of the toothbrush bristles gently scrubbing your teeth; the smell of your shampoo as you lather it into your hair; the cars and scenery around you as you navigate familiar streets... If your mind strays to planning what you'll cook for dinner or mentally preparing for a meeting, gently guide it back to the present.

2 **WALK MINDFULLY.** Whether you're walking for exercise or just to get from one place to the next, use this time to focus on the rhythm and movement rather than planning your to-do list or replaying conversations in your head. Focus on the repetition and sound of your footsteps, the feeling of the grass or pavement under your feet, the breeze or rain on your skin, the people and buildings around you. Keep your focus on you in this moment, until you reach your destination.

3 **EAT MINDFULLY.** With many of us eating on the run, at our desks or in front of the television, we can easily consume an entire meal without tasting it. Aim to enjoy meals at a table, away from screens and other distractions. Chew and taste every bite, paying attention to the flavours, smells, colours and textures, and appreciating the time and effort that went into its preparation. Put down your cutlery in between bites to allow time to enjoy every mouthful. Listen to your body and stop eating when you're full.

What is a mental health check?

If you're feeling troubled, down or suffering from symptoms of anxiety or depression, the first step to getting help is to talk to your GP. They can conduct an initial mental health assessment, which usually involves a series of questions and a physical examination. Based on this assessment, they may then refer you to a counsellor, psychologist or psychiatrist for further treatment.

WHAT TO EXPECT

When booking your appointment, be sure to mention it's for a mental health check so the receptionist can allocate sufficient time. For the interview component, your doctor will ask about your personal history, including your work, relationship, family and home environments. They'll also ask about any current or past events (traumatic or otherwise) that may be contributing to your current state of mind, and if you drink alcohol, smoke, take drugs or are on any medications. As a priority, they'll determine if you're at risk of hurting yourself or others. It's important to answer these questions as truthfully as possible to give the best chances of an accurate diagnosis.

For the physical examination, your GP may check your blood pressure and heart rate. You'll be asked about any family history of mental illness, and they may order blood or urine tests to check for other contributing causes.

WHAT HAPPENS NEXT?

Based on the information gathered in this initial assessment, your GP will create a mental health treatment plan based on your needs, circumstances, condition and preferences. You may benefit from some lifestyle changes, therapy or medication, or a combination of all three.

Currently a mental health treatment plan allows you to claim up to 20 sessions with a mental health professional per calendar year under Medicare.

> **If you are in crisis and need immediate support, call Triple Zero (000) or Lifeline on 13 11 14.**

Mood-friendly food swaps

It's no secret that some highly processed foods can be bad for our long-term health, and there is one group of foods to reduce in particular: ultra-processed foods (UPFs). A study by Deakin University's Food & Mood Centre has found that people who eat high amounts of UPFs have a 22 per cent greater chance of developing depression. UPFs are highly refined and often have a lot of added sugar, salt, oils and fats along with artificial colours and preservatives. See below for some healthy alternatives to common UPFs.

NOT SO GOOD (Ultra-processed foods)	BETTER (Processed foods)	BEST (Less processed)
Sweetened breakfast cereals	Bran-based cereal	Homemade porridge with berries
White bread	Wholegrain bread	Homemade sourdough
Soft drink	Flavoured sparkling water	Iced water with lime wedges
Flavoured potato chips	Plain tortilla chips	Homemade pita chips
Fried chicken	Deli rotisserie chicken	Homemade roast chicken
French fries	Potato wedges	Baked potato
Packaged biscuits	Homemade biscuits	A handful of nuts
Chocolate dairy desserts	Flavoured yoghurt	Greek yoghurt with fruit
Hot dogs	Low-sodium sausages	Lean mince or chicken breast
Flavoured muesli bars	Low-sugar granola bars	Roasted nuts or chickpeas
Microwave popcorn	Air-popped popcorn	Corn kernels popped on the stove

AUGUST

S	M	T	W	T	F	S
		1	2	3	4	5
6	7	8	9	10	11	12
13	14	15	16	17	18	19
20	21	22	23	24	25	26
27	28	29	30	31		

SEPTEMBER

S	M	T	W	T	F	S
					1	2
3	4	5	6	7	8	9
10	11	12	13	14	15	16
17	18	19	20	21	22	23
24	25	26	27	28	29	30

OCTOBER

S	M	T	W	T	F	S
1	2	3	4	5	6	7
8	9	10	11	12	13	14
15	16	17	18	19	20	21
22	23	24	25	26	27	28
29	30	31				

28 MONDAY

29 TUESDAY

30 WEDNESDAY

31 THURSDAY

September
2023

1 FRIDAY INDIGENOUS LITERACY DAY

2 SATURDAY

> **SOCIAL ENGAGEMENT** is crucial for our wellbeing. Make time every day to speak with family, catch-up with friends or join community groups and activities.

3 SUNDAY FATHER'S DAY

AUGUST

S	M	T	W	T	F	S
		1	2	3	4	5
6	7	8	9	10	11	12
13	14	15	16	17	18	19
20	21	22	23	24	25	26
27	28	29	30	31		

SEPTEMBER

S	M	T	W	T	F	S
					1	2
3	4	5	6	7	8	9
10	11	12	13	14	15	16
17	18	19	20	21	22	23
24	25	26	27	28	29	30

OCTOBER

S	M	T	W	T	F	S
1	2	3	4	5	6	7
8	9	10	11	12	13	14
15	16	17	18	19	20	21
22	23	24	25	26	27	28
29	30	31				

4 MONDAY

5 TUESDAY

6 WEDNESDAY

7 THURSDAY

September
2023

8 FRIDAY

9 SATURDAY

10 SUNDAY

AUGUST						
S	M	T	W	T	F	S
		1	2	3	4	5
6	7	8	9	10	11	12
13	14	15	16	17	18	19
20	21	22	23	24	25	26
27	28	29	30	31		

SEPTEMBER						
S	M	T	W	T	F	S
					1	2
3	4	5	6	7	8	9
10	11	12	13	14	15	16
17	18	19	20	21	22	23
24	25	26	27	28	29	30

OCTOBER						
S	M	T	W	T	F	S
1	2	3	4	5	6	7
8	9	10	11	12	13	14
15	16	17	18	19	20	21
22	23	24	25	26	27	28
29	30	31				

11 MONDAY

12 TUESDAY

13 WEDNESDAY

14 THURSDAY R U OK? DAY

15 FRIDAY   ROSH HASHANAH (JEWISH NEW YEAR)

SPENDING TIME WITH ANIMALS has been shown to stimulate feelings of happiness. If you don't have a pet, visit friends who do, volunteer with a wildlife organisation or go to the zoo.

16 SATURDAY

17 SUNDAY

AUGUST						
S	M	T	W	T	F	S
		1	2	3	4	5
6	7	8	9	10	11	12
13	14	15	16	17	18	19
20	21	22	23	24	25	26
27	28	29	30	31		

SEPTEMBER						
S	M	T	W	T	F	S
					1	2
3	4	5	6	7	8	9
10	11	12	13	14	15	16
17	18	19	20	21	22	23
24	25	26	27	28	29	30

OCTOBER						
S	M	T	W	T	F	S
1	2	3	4	5	6	7
8	9	10	11	12	13	14
15	16	17	18	19	20	21
22	23	24	25	26	27	28
29	30	31				

18 MONDAY

19 TUESDAY

20 WEDNESDAY

21 THURSDAY

September
2023

22 FRIDAY

23 SATURDAY

TAKE REGULAR TECHNOLOGY BREAKS to limit mindless scrolling. Try putting your phone in another room, disabling social media apps or having periods of 'quiet time'.

24 SUNDAY

| A U G U S T | | | | | | |
S	M	T	W	T	F	S
		1	2	3	4	5
6	7	8	9	10	11	12
13	14	15	16	17	18	19
20	21	22	23	24	25	26
27	28	29	30	31		

| S E P T E M B E R | | | | | | |
S	M	T	W	T	F	S
					1	2
3	4	5	6	7	8	9
10	11	12	13	14	15	16
17	18	19	20	21	22	23
24	25	26	27	28	29	30

| O C T O B E R | | | | | | |
S	M	T	W	T	F	S
1	2	3	4	5	6	7
8	9	10	11	12	13	14
15	16	17	18	19	20	21
22	23	24	25	26	27	28
29	30	31				

25 MONDAY QUEEN'S BIRTHDAY (WA), YOM KIPPUR (JEWISH HOLY DAY)

26 TUESDAY

27 WEDNESDAY EID MILAD UN NABI (PROPHET'S BIRTHDAY)

28 THURSDAY

September-October
2023

29 FRIDAY

30 SATURDAY

TUNE IN TO THE BREAST CANCER TRIALS PODCAST to hear the latest breast cancer research findings, as well as people's experiences with the disease. Available from your favourite podcast platform.

1 SUNDAY BREAST CANCER AWARENESS MONTH

It was heartbreaking and probably the worst part – the thought of my kids losing their mum. They give me the strength to push through on the days when I feel like giving up. When treatment is done, we need to spend more 'fun' time together.

Shalu Singh, diagnosed at age 43

let's talk about
BREAST HEALTH

It's estimated more than 200,000 Australian women are living with breast cancer today. Give yourself and your loved ones the best chance of survival by knowing the signs of breast cancer and eliminating unhealthy habits.

Breast cancer is not one disease, but several. It includes several subtypes, and as such, treatments can be personalised to the patient, their age and circumstances. These are the most common forms of breast cancer.

THE TYPES OF BREAST CANCER
Non-invasive breast cancers are contained within an area of the breast and have not grown into the normal breast tissue. These do not have the ability to spread to other parts of the body. However, if left untreated, they may become invasive over time. Surgery to remove the affected tissue or the entire breast is usually performed to prevent the cancer from becoming invasive. Non-invasive breast cancers include:
- **Ductal carcinoma in situ** (DCIS), confined to the ducts of the breast
- **Lobular carcinoma in situ** (LCIS), confined to the lobules (milk glands) of the breast.

Invasive breast cancers grow in the normal breast tissue with the potential to spread to other areas of the body. Treatment depends on how advanced the cancer is (the stage of the cancer) and other factors. Surgery may be recommended, along with other types of treatment either before or after surgery, or both. Invasive breast cancer can present in different ways, including:

- **Early breast cancer**, contained in the breast, which may or may not spread to the lymph nodes in the breast or armpit
- **Inflammatory breast cancer**, a rare form that affects lymphatic vessels in the breast skin, causing redness and inflammation
- **Paget's disease of the nipple**, a rare form of breast cancer that affects the nipple and the areola; commonly associated with an invasive cancer elsewhere in the breast
- **Locally advanced breast cancer**, which has spread to areas near the breast, such as the chest wall
- **Metastatic breast cancer** (also called advanced, secondary or stage 4 breast cancer), that has spread from the breast to other parts of the body, such as the bones, liver or lungs.

The following are different types of breast cancer, each requiring different treatments:
- **HER2-positive breast cancer**, any type of breast cancer that tests positive for a protein called human epidermal growth factor receptor 2 (HER2)
- **Triple negative breast cancer**, a type of breast cancer that tests negative for all three receptors – oestrogen, progesterone and HER2
- **Hormone receptor positive** – oestrogen and/or progesterone receptors are present in the breast cancer cells.

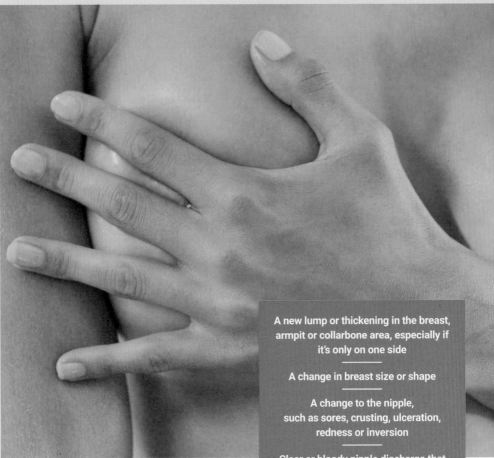

The signs and symptoms of breast cancer

Breast awareness is important for women of all ages, even if you're having regular mammograms. By getting to know the regular shape and feel of your breasts, you'll be better equipped to notice any significant changes as they occur, which may indicate cancer. The symptoms of breast cancer will vary depending on where the tumour is within the breast, the size of the tumour and how quickly it is growing, but any of the following should be investigated further:

A new lump or thickening in the breast, armpit or collarbone area, especially if it's only on one side

A change in breast size or shape

A change to the nipple, such as sores, crusting, ulceration, redness or inversion

Clear or bloody nipple discharge that occurs without squeezing

A change in the skin of the breast such as redness, puckering or dimpling

An unusual tenderness, pain or swelling in the breast or armpit that doesn't go away

Remember, nine out of 10 breast changes aren't due to cancer. A number of conditions can cause these changes, and pregnancy, weight gain or loss and age can alter the shape, feel and size of your breasts. Regardless, it's always best to consult your doctor if you notice any changes in your breasts.

Understanding your breast cancer risk

There are certain physiological and lifestyle factors that can put us at greater risk of breast cancer. Some of these can be changed, and some can't. Having a risk factor, or even several risk factors, doesn't mean you will be diagnosed with breast cancer. For instance, only five to 10 per cent of breast cancers are associated with a strong family history or known genetic mutation. But awareness and early detection is the key to survival, so it's important to note the following risks.

BEING FEMALE It's predicted that around 20,000 women will be diagnosed with breast cancer this year. Starting your period before the age of 12, going through menopause after the age of 55, not having children or having them when you're 30 or older can also slightly increase the risk.

INCREASING AGE Although breast cancer can occur in younger women, over 75 per cent of all breast cancers in Australia are diagnosed in women when they're aged 50 years or over. The average age of first diagnosis in women is 61.

FAMILY HISTORY Women with one first-degree relative (parent, sibling or child) who has had breast cancer have almost two times the risk of breast cancer as those with no family history, particularly if the relative was diagnosed before the age of 50. The risk increases with each additional family member diagnosed with breast cancer. Inheritance of mutations in the genes such as BRCA1, BRCA2, PALB2 and CHEK2 can also increase the risk significantly.

BEING OVERWEIGHT Breast cancer risk increases in postmenopausal women by about six per cent for every five kilograms of weight above a normal healthy weight range. You can combat this by eating a healthy diet and doing regular exercise.

DRINKING ALCOHOL Women who drink one standard glass of alcohol each day have a seven per cent higher risk of breast cancer than those who never drink alcohol, and this risk increases with additional consumption. While reducing your alcohol intake can help reduce your overall risk, switching to non-alcoholic options or avoiding it altogether is the best strategy.

SMOKING Studies have shown that smoking can increase your risk of many serious health issues including breast cancer. Seek help from Quitline on 137 848 to give up smoking for good.

MEDICAL HISTORY A previous breast cancer diagnosis or past history of certain non-cancerous breast conditions can also put you at increased risk.

The screening tools for breast cancer

Finding breast cancer early increases your treatment options and chances of survival. Part of this is knowing your risk factors and watching for breast changes, and for women who have no symptoms, tests and scans can also be invaluable for early detection. These are the main options for detecting and diagnosing breast cancer.

PHYSICAL EXAMINATION If you notice any breast changes, your doctor may perform a physical examination to check both breasts and the lymph nodes around your collarbone and under your arms.

TOMOSYNTHESIS Also known as a three-dimensional mammography or digital breast tomosynthesis (DBT), X-rays are taken from different angles to make a three-dimensional image. Sometimes used to find small breast cancers, particularly in women with dense breast tissue.

ULTRASOUND This non-invasive scan uses sound waves to create a complete picture of your breast. It's an important tool for women who have dense breast tissue.

BIOPSY If breast cancer is suspected, a doctor will remove a sample of breast tissue with a needle for pathology examination under a microscope.

MRI SCAN Mainly used for people at high risk of breast cancer or those who have very dense breast tissue or implants, or when previous imaging test results are unclear. A magnetic resonance imaging (MRI) scan uses a large magnet and radio waves to create a computer image of the breast tissue.

CT, BONE AND/OR PET SCAN If breast cancer is detected, your specialist may order additional scans to see if it has spread to other parts of the body.

MAMMOGRAM

Women aged 50-74 are invited to receive a free two-yearly screening mammogram through BreastScreen Australia. If you're aged 40-49 or 75 and over, you are also eligible for free screening mammograms, but won't receive a reminder. This low-dose X-ray of the breast tissue can detect changes that are too small to be felt during a physical examination.

CELEBRATING ITS 25TH YEAR, The Australian Women's Health Diary wouldn't be where it is today without the support of you, its loyal readers. Funds raised by the purchase of this diary go towards funding extremely important and life-changing breast cancer research at Breast Cancer Trials.

The proud legacy behind this diary

One of the many researchers working with Breast Cancer Trials, oncologist Dr Nick Zdenkowski, explains how these funds can improve women's breast cancer outcomes.

WHAT ARE CLINICAL TRIALS?

A clinical trial looks at new forms of treatment to determine if they're better than the current standard of care. Trials also investigate new detection and diagnostic methods and prevention strategies for those considered high risk. Currently breast cancer has a significant impact – physically, emotionally and financially – on those diagnosed and their families. The overall aim of our research is to save lives and improve quality of life.

HOW DO TRIALS CHANGE LIVES?

The breast cancer treatments available today are saving lives as a result of past clinical trials. And the research that we're currently conducting will influence how breast cancer is managed in the future – this is one of the main motivators for the women who participate in our trials.

One recent breakthrough has seen the benefits of giving additional chemotherapy after surgery for those whose breast cancer did not shrink with chemotherapy given prior to surgery. An online patient support tool developed by Breast Cancer Trials (myneoguide.com) can help women with early-stage breast cancer understand their options to make an informed decision.

WHAT IS BREAST CANCER TRIALS CURRENTLY WORKING ON?

There are several important research areas in the works. Our Neo-N clinical trial aims to find out if giving an immunotherapy drug in combination with chemotherapy can harness a person's immune system against their cancer, and spare them from the need for some of the harsher chemotherapies.

Another fascinating trial, BRCA-P aims to find out if we can prevent breast cancer from occurring in women at high risk due to having the BRCA1 gene mutation. This international trial, co-led by one of our Breast Cancer Trials researchers, is repurposing a drug used for osteoporosis to potentially stop pre-cancerous cells in their tracks.

Our EXPERT and OPTIMA clinical trials are leveraging the use of tumour genomic testing to see if some patients can be spared from radiotherapy and chemotherapy without compromise to their survival. And of course, ongoing research is needed to stop breast cancer from recurring, to maintain good quality of life post treatment and to prolong life. The sales of this diary will assist in this process.

For more information about breast cancer, contact Breast Cancer Trials; breastcancertrials.org.au

SEPTEMBER

S	M	T	W	T	F	S
					1	2
3	4	5	6	7	8	9
10	11	12	13	14	15	16
17	18	19	20	21	22	23
24	25	26	27	28	29	30

OCTOBER

S	M	T	W	T	F	S
1	2	3	4	5	6	7
8	9	10	11	12	13	14
15	16	17	18	19	20	21
22	23	24	25	26	27	28
29	30	31				

NOVEMBER

S	M	T	W	T	F	S
			1	2	3	4
5	6	7	8	9	10	11
12	13	14	15	16	17	18
19	20	21	22	23	24	25
26	27	28	29	30		

2 MONDAY LABOUR DAY (ACT, NSW, SA), QUEEN'S BIRTHDAY (QLD)

3 TUESDAY

4 WEDNESDAY

5 THURSDAY

October
2023

6 FRIDAY

7 SATURDAY

8 SUNDAY

SEPTEMBER						
S	M	T	W	T	F	S
					1	2
3	4	5	6	7	8	9
10	11	12	13	14	15	16
17	18	19	20	21	22	23
24	25	26	27	28	29	30

OCTOBER						
S	M	T	W	T	F	S
1	2	3	4	5	6	7
8	9	10	11	12	13	14
15	16	17	18	19	20	21
22	23	24	25	26	27	28
29	30	31				

NOVEMBER						
S	M	T	W	T	F	S
			1	2	3	4
5	6	7	8	9	10	11
12	13	14	15	16	17	18
19	20	21	22	23	24	25
26	27	28	29	30		

9 MONDAY

10 TUESDAY

11 WEDNESDAY

12 THURSDAY

13 FRIDAY

14 SATURDAY

> **IF SOMEONE YOU KNOW HAS BEEN DIAGNOSED** with breast cancer, don't be afraid that you won't know what to say or how to support them. Just be yourself.

15 SUNDAY

SEPTEMBER						
S	M	T	W	T	F	S
					1	2
3	4	5	6	7	8	9
10	11	12	13	14	15	16
17	18	19	20	21	22	23
24	25	26	27	28	29	30

OCTOBER						
S	M	T	W	T	F	S
1	2	3	4	5	6	7
8	9	10	11	12	13	14
15	16	17	18	19	20	21
22	23	24	25	26	27	28
29	30	31				

NOVEMBER						
S	M	T	W	T	F	S
			1	2	3	4
5	6	7	8	9	10	11
12	13	14	15	16	17	18
19	20	21	22	23	24	25
26	27	28	29	30		

16 MONDAY

17 TUESDAY

18 WEDNESDAY

19 THURSDAY

20 FRIDAY

21 SATURDAY

22 SUNDAY

S	E	P	T	E	M	B	E	R
S	M	T	W	T	F	S
					1	2
3	4	5	6	7	8	9
10	11	12	13	14	15	16
17	18	19	20	21	22	23
24	25	26	27	28	29	30

O	C	T	O	B	E	R
S	M	T	W	T	F	S
1	2	3	4	5	6	7
8	9	10	11	12	13	14
15	16	17	18	19	20	21
22	23	24	25	26	27	28
29	30	31

N	O	V	E	M	B	E	R
S	M	T	W	T	F	S
			1	2	3	4
5	6	7	8	9	10	11
12	13	14	15	16	17	18
19	20	21	22	23	24	25
26	27	28	29	30

23 MONDAY AUSTRALIA'S BREAST CANCER DAY

24 TUESDAY

25 WEDNESDAY

26 THURSDAY ROYAL HOBART SHOW (TAS)

27 FRIDAY

28 SATURDAY

RESEARCH SHOWS REGULAR EXERCISE can help prevent breast cancer by boosting immune function, warding off obesity and lowering oestrogen levels. Aim for at least 30 minutes of exercise each day.

29 SUNDAY

66

I was first diagnosed five years ago with a small tumour and had surgery. This time, my lymph nodes showed some cancer cells. The severe side effects of chemotherapy have left me feeling very low, but the constant flowers from loved ones are my sunshine in a vase.

Stef Kinsey, first diagnosed at age 60

let's talk about
HEALTHY SKIN

As the body's largest organ, our skin is susceptible to freckles, moles, wrinkles, acne and UV damage. Don't underestimate the importance of sun safety, regular skin checks and seeking help for visible skin conditions.

Some would say that adult acne is one of life's great injustices – breakouts continuing beyond the teenage years, and with greater severity. Usually appearing around the jawline, chin and neck, these pimples tend to be deeper and more painful than the ones experienced during puberty, and can remain active for many years into our 30s and 40s. To add to the unfairness of the situation, adult acne affects more women than men.

WHAT CAUSES ADULT ACNE?

While teenage acne is primarily caused by hormonal changes, adult acne can be a sign that something is off-kilter within your body. Stress, diet, family history and hormonal imbalances can all play a part, along with some health conditions like polycystic ovarian syndrome (PCOS). It's also common for women to experience acne flare-ups in the week before each menstrual cycle.

HOW TO TREAT IT

It's important to understand that adult skin is often drier and more sensitive than teenaged skin, so the acne solutions that worked in your teens most likely won't help as an adult. You'll need a treatment plan tailored to you and your skin type, and the first step is to have your acne assessed by a doctor or skin specialist so the cause can be identified and treated. Most GPs will treat mild or moderate acne by prescribing the oral contraceptive pill, over-the-counter treatments or topical therapies, such as creams and gels containing antibiotics or retonoids. For more severe cases, you may be referred to a dermatologist, who will take a holistic approach and consider the physical implications as well as the social and emotional impact of your acne. They can also provide guidance on the right skincare products to complement your acne treatment plan.

THE EMOTIONAL EFFECTS

Due to its visible nature, acne can have a significant psychological impact. Some sufferers feel embarrassed by their acne or acne-related scars, to the point that it prevents them from going out and doing the things they love. For this very reason, it's important to seek treatment for your acne early, to potentially reduce the risk of permanent physical scars and help with any emotional distress.

For more information, visit The Australasian College of Dermatologists; dermcoll.edu.au

Simple sun-safe habits to adopt

For the best protection against Australia's high UV levels, take these five SunSmart steps.

1 Slip on some protective clothing to cover as much skin as possible. This could be a long-sleeved, collared shirt and pants while you're gardening or a rash vest for swimming. Loose, opaque or quick-dry fabrics in a darker shade tend to be most effective. If shopping for clothing for this purpose, check the label for an ultraviolet protection factor (UPF) of 30 or above – this is a guarantee of how much UV protection the fabric provides.

2 Slop on a generous amount of SPF 30 (or higher) broad-spectrum, water-resistant sunscreen at least 20 minutes before going outside. Apply to clean, dry skin, and remember to reapply every two hours or after swimming or excessive sweating. Many people think sunscreen alone will protect them from the sun's harsh rays, but it needs to be used in conjunction with the other four steps.

3 Slide on a pair of close-fitting, wrap-around sunglasses (to be worn outside during daylight hours) that meet the Australian Standard AS/NSZ 1067. When paired with a broad-brimmed hat, sunglasses can reduce UV radiation exposure to the eyes by up to 98 per cent.

A NOTE ON AEROSOL SUNSCREENS
They're fast and easy to apply, especially on wriggling children and hard to reach places. However, off the back of new research, Cancer Council Australia advises against the use of aerosol sunscreens. Due to their spray nature, it's difficult to gauge whether you're getting the right amount of coverage and UV protection. As well, strong winds can cause some of the spray to be lost.

Instead, cream or lotion sunscreens are deemed much safer, as you can measure how much is being applied and where it's going. As a guide, seven teaspoons of lotion will cover the average adult body – one teaspoon per arm and leg (four total), one for the front torso, one for the back and one for the face, neck and ears.

4 Seek shade provided by dense tree foliage, built structures or portable options like shade tents and umbrellas. Just remember, shade moves with the sun, so be prepared to follow it if you're outdoors for a long period.

CHECK YOUR SPOTS Your best defence against skin cancer is to become familiar with your skin and check it regularly for any changes to existing freckles or moles and new spots. Look for changes in colour, size and shape, as well as scaliness, ulceration, bleeding or spots that are painful to the touch. And make sure you check all areas of your skin, not just those that are exposed to the sun. Use a full-length or hand mirror or ask a family member for help. If you notice any changes, see your GP straightaway.

For more information, visit Cancer Council; cancer.org.au

5 Slap on a broad-brim, bucket or legionnaire style hat to shade your head, neck, ears and face. Check the weave and material – if it's loosely constructed, the UV rays can still get through. Avoid caps and visors, which don't provide adequate protection.

The truth about skin cancer

Approximately 2000 Australians die from skin cancer each year, and two in three adults will be diagnosed with some form of it by the age of 70. Don't be complacent – arm yourself with the following facts to protect your skin from the sun's harmful rays.

FACT: Tanning is just one cause of skin cancer

You can also be exposed to UV rays while going about your normal day – for instance, going for a walk, playing soccer with the kids or gardening outdoors.

FACT: Skin cancer does not discriminate

While those with a pale complexion and lots of freckles and moles do have a higher risk of melanoma, you're not immune to UV radiation if you have a darker complexion.

FACT: You can still get sunburnt on a cloudy day

You may not feel the heat, but the damaging UV rays are still there. Check daily UV levels in your area on the SunSmart app, Bureau of Meteorology website or in the newspaper weather section, and take appropriate sun-safe precautions if levels are 3 or above.

FACT: Not all sunscreens are created equal

There's little difference between SPF30 and SPF50 products, but only broad-spectrum sunscreens will protect against both UVA and UVB rays. Use sunscreen before its expiration date for full efficacy.

FACT: You can get sunburnt in the car

UV rays can penetrate glass, especially side windows. Reduce your exposure by keeping the windows up and wearing sunscreen and sun-protective clothing.

FACT: Skin cancers aren't always easy to remove

Depending on where the cancer is and how long it's been there, treatment can be invasive, involving surgery, chemotherapy and scarring.

FACT: It's never too late to practise sun-safe habits

Whether you're 16 or 60, you can reduce your risk of skin cancer by adopting all five forms of sun protection (see previous page) when UV levels are 3 and above.

We're committed to carbon neutral parcel delivery

Find out how at
auspost.com.au/carbon-neutral

OCTOBER
S	M	T	W	T	F	S
1	2	3	4	5	6	7
8	9	10	11	12	13	14
15	16	17	18	19	20	21
22	23	24	25	26	27	28
29	30	31				

NOVEMBER
S	M	T	W	T	F	S
			1	2	3	4
5	6	7	8	9	10	11
12	13	14	15	16	17	18
19	20	21	22	23	24	25
26	27	28	29	30		

DECEMBER
S	M	T	W	T	F	S
31					1	2
3	4	5	6	7	8	9
10	11	12	13	14	15	16
17	18	19	20	21	22	23
24	25	26	27	28	29	30

30 MONDAY

31 TUESDAY HALLOWEEN

1 WEDNESDAY

2 THURSDAY

3 FRIDAY

4 SATURDAY

IF YOU LIVE OR ARE HOLIDAYING IN QUEENSLAND, sun protection is needed year round due to consistently high UV levels. Slip, Slop, Slap, Slide and Seek Shade.

5 SUNDAY

OCTOBER

S	M	T	W	T	F	S
1	2	3	4	5	6	7
8	9	10	11	12	13	14
15	16	17	18	19	20	21
22	23	24	25	26	27	28
29	30	31				

NOVEMBER

S	M	T	W	T	F	S
			1	2	3	4
5	6	7	8	9	10	11
12	13	14	15	16	17	18
19	20	21	22	23	24	25
26	27	28	29	30		

DECEMBER

S	M	T	W	T	F	S
31					1	2
3	4	5	6	7	8	9
10	11	12	13	14	15	16
17	18	19	20	21	22	23
24	25	26	27	28	29	30

6 MONDAY RECREATION DAY (TAS)

7 TUESDAY MELBOURNE CUP (VIC)

8 WEDNESDAY

9 THURSDAY

November
2023

10 FRIDAY

11 SATURDAY REMEMBRANCE DAY

DON'T WASTE MONEY ON COLLAGEN supplements to improve skin health. Experts say drinking water and eating a diet rich in wholefoods and protein will do the same job.

12 SUNDAY DIWALI (HINDU, BUDDHIST, JAIN AND SIKH FESTIVAL)

OCTOBER

S	M	T	W	T	F	S
1	2	3	4	5	6	7
8	9	10	11	12	13	14
15	16	17	18	19	20	21
22	23	24	25	26	27	28
29	30	31				

NOVEMBER

S	M	T	W	T	F	S
			1	2	3	4
5	6	7	8	9	10	11
12	13	14	15	16	17	18
19	20	21	22	23	24	25
26	27	28	29	30		

DECEMBER

S	M	T	W	T	F	S
31					1	2
3	4	5	6	7	8	9
10	11	12	13	14	15	16
17	18	19	20	21	22	23
24	25	26	27	28	29	30

13 MONDAY

14 TUESDAY

15 WEDNESDAY

16 THURSDAY

17 FRIDAY

18 SATURDAY

DONATE TO BREAST CANCER RESEARCH in your will to help create a future where breast cancer has no power over women's lives. Visit breastcancertrials. org.au for more information.

19 SUNDAY

OCTOBER

S	M	T	W	T	F	S
1	2	3	4	5	6	7
8	9	10	11	12	13	14
15	16	17	18	19	20	21
22	23	24	25	26	27	28
29	30	31				

NOVEMBER

S	M	T	W	T	F	S
			1	2	3	4
5	6	7	8	9	10	11
12	13	14	15	16	17	18
19	20	21	22	23	24	25
26	27	28	29	30		

DECEMBER

S	M	T	W	T	F	S
31					1	2
3	4	5	6	7	8	9
10	11	12	13	14	15	16
17	18	19	20	21	22	23
24	25	26	27	28	29	30

20 MONDAY

21 TUESDAY

22 WEDNESDAY

23 THURSDAY

24 FRIDAY

25 SATURDAY

MAKE PUTTING ON SUNSCREEN a fun part of your child's routine by drawing dots or squiggles of sunscreen on their face and limbs for them to carefully rub in.

26 SUNDAY

"

From age 21 I knew I carried the BRCA1 gene mutation and a 70 per cent risk of breast cancer. My diagnosis came earlier than anyone expected and was still a shock after years of careful surveillance. I'm proud to have participated in a clinical trial, which made a major breakthrough in treatment.

Dimity Paul, diagnosed at age 31

let's talk about LIFESTYLE

As the year draws to an end, resolve to make healthier choices in all areas of your life, from sustainable practices and seasonal eating to a more balanced approach to travel and technology.

You may be familiar with the term sustainability, which advocates living in a way that benefits our health, cuts costs and safeguards the environment for future generations. Living sustainably doesn't mean going without the things you love and enjoy, but rather forming new habits and making better choices that work in with your lifestyle. Try these ideas.

1 REDUCE ENERGY USE Turn off lights and appliances when not in use, install energy-efficient appliances, hang washing out to dry, cool and ventilate your home naturally or use LED light globes.

2 SAVE WATER Choose water-efficient appliances and water-saving tap and shower fittings, fix leaking taps, grow drought-tolerant plants or install a water tank.

3 SHOP LOCALLY The less distance a product travels to reach you, the better. Buy fresh produce from local growers and markets or grow your own. Purchase locally manufactured clothing and household goods.

4 BANISH SINGLE-USE ITEMS Look for reusable alternatives to disposable cups, cutlery and dinnerware and plastic cotton buds, straws and water bottles.

5 TRY A CLIMATARIAN DIET Reduce your carbon footprint by eating plant-based foods, cutting down on meat and avoiding farmed fish and foods containing palm oil (linked with deforestation).

6 AVOID FOOD WASTE Plan meals based on what's in the fridge and freezer, store food correctly so it lasts longer and dispose of fruit and vegetable scraps in a worm farm.

7 REUSE, REHOME, RECYCLE Think of an alternate use for items you no longer need. Reuse plastic bottles as vases, broken pots as plant markers or old T-shirts as a pull toy for your dog. Donate good-quality items to another family or charity, and investigate local recycling drop-off points or collection options to dispose of batteries, electronics, soft plastics, paint, gas bottles and more.

8 DRIVE LESS Lower fuel costs and emissions by taking public transport, carpooling or walking short distances.

9 SUPPORT FAIR TRADE Look for fair-trade certification on imported goods – particularly coffee, cocoa, sugar, tea, chocolate and fruit – to ensure they were grown using sustainable methods and their producers were paid adequately.

Summer meal ideas for when it's too hot to cook

Sweltering temperatures can play havoc with our appetite and motivation levels. Enjoy the abundance of fresh summer produce on offer with these simple meals – no oven required.

BREAKFAST

Eat your oats cold. Combine ½ cup rolled oats, ½ cup Greek yoghurt, ¼ cup coconut milk and 1 teaspoon maple syrup and leave overnight. Top with mango and berries.

Whip up a tropical smoothie by blitzing ½ cup pineapple, ½ cup mango, ½ banana, 1 cup of almond milk, mint leaves and a few ice cubes (optional) in the blender.

Swap your toast for a wrap, and experiment with fresh fillings. Try salmon and avocado, peanut butter with banana or kiwifruit or ricotta, honey and fresh figs.

LUNCH

Make a salad from mixed leaves, canned lentils (rinsed), cherry tomatoes, red onion, fetta and chopped walnuts. Dress with lemon juice, Dijon mustard and olive oil.

You can't go past a sandwich. Spread grainy bread with hummus or avocado and top with cooked chicken, tuna or turkey, tomato, cheese, lettuce or grated carrot.

Put together a ploughman's platter of sliced roast beef or low-sodium ham, tzatziki, tomato, olives, Swiss cheese, pesto and wholemeal pita bread or sliced sourdough.

DINNER

Try Gazpacho, a chilled soup from Spain. It's made from bread soaked in water, onion, tomato, cucumber, capsicum, garlic, oil and vinegar, all blended together.

Showcase fresh summer ingredients by topping lettuce leaves with cooked, peeled prawns, diced mango, diced avocado, shaved cucumber, coriander, lime and chilli.

Make rice paper rolls filled with thinly sliced carrot, bean sprouts, fresh coriander and cooked chicken or tofu. Note: you'll need boiled water to soften the rice paper wraps.

Tips for a healthy holiday

As the year comes to an end, you may be looking forward to some time away on holiday. Rather than letting go of your healthy habits, why not build them into your break, and combat any festive season overindulgence at the same time? Wellness holidays, such as yoga retreats, walking or cycling tours, dietary detoxes and luxury day spa packages, are designed for this very purpose. They focus on the main pillars of health – diet, exercise or mental wellbeing – to help holidaymakers kick-start or cement a healthy lifestyle for the long-term. Take a similar approach by building health-focused intentions into your holiday. Here's how.

Your holiday focus: HEALTHY DIET

- Book accommodation with cooking facilities so you don't need to eat out for every meal.
- Bring your own healthy snacks to avoid the lure of the minibar.
- Shop for fresh produce at markets, seafood co-ops or local growers.
- Research dining options beforehand, to find restaurants that favour fresh fare.
- Use this holiday as an opportunity to reduce or cut out alcohol or caffeine.

Your holiday focus: MOVEMENT

- If staying at a resort, make use of the on-site gym, pool or tennis courts.
- Sign up for local yoga or Pilates classes.
- Go for daily walks on the beach, between sights or along scenic bush or rainforest tracks.
- Too far to walk? Hire bikes to get from A to B.
- Plan at least one active activity each day, such as golf, kayaking, beach cricket, snorkelling, lawn bowls, yoga, surfing, volleyball – you name it!

Your holiday focus: MENTAL WELLBEING

- Book an off-grid cabin or hitch a tent in a spot surrounded by nature.
- Switch off from digital technology and work communications as much as possible.
- Sleep! With no tight schedule to stick to, take the opportunity to enjoy morning sleep-ins or afternoon siestas.
- Read a book, meditate or keep a holiday journal.
- Book in for a massage or some pampering at a local day spa.

The pros and cons of social media

There are currently 20.5 million active social media users in Australia, or 79.9 per cent of the population. On average, people aged 16 to 64 spend 106 minutes per day interacting with social media, be it reading news articles on Facebook, watching YouTube cooking videos, liking friends' photos on Instagram or chuckling at the latest TikTok dance craze. And while there is a lot to be gained from this daily interaction, there are also negative implications to such heavy reliance on technology. Here we list the good with the bad.

THE PROS

- Social media gives us the ability to stay in touch with friends and loved ones all around the world and to nurture relationships with those we can't physically visit.
- It can be a great space to chat with like-minded people and potentially form new friendships that can be continued offline.
- Many see it as a safe space to seek advice, recommendations or support, particularly those in remote locations.
- Some social media users feel they can come out of their shells and express their true identities online, with feedback in the form of likes bolstering their self-confidence.
- Many users rely on social media to stay informed of current issues and news stories.
- It can broaden our perspectives and expose us to new ideas and views.
- Social media can lift the mood and be a form of stress-management as well as a creative outlet.

THE CONS

- Connecting digitally can have a negative impact on face-to-face interactions, leading to feelings of isolation. A person with thousands of followers can still feel alone.
- Seeing the highlight reels of other people's lives can contribute to feelings of inadequacy, low self-esteem and negative body image, putting us at risk of depression and anxiety.
- Cyberbullying and trolling are a major issue, with some people using the shield of technology to harass, bully and intimidate others.
- Some social media users present inauthentic versions of themselves.
- Low or no feedback on posts can lead to a lack of self-worth or feelings of rejection, especially in teens.
- The temptation to constantly check social media can distract us from work, study and more worthwhile pursuits, and interfere with sleep.
- Users can be at risk of falling victim to online scammers and predators.

THE VERDICT To enjoy the benefits of social media minus the negative implications, it's important to place limits on the amount of time we engage with it and ensure we're using it for the right reasons (to connect, to learn, to gain information). Beware of fake news and never seek medical or financial advice on social media. Most importantly, balance it with real-world activities, face-to-face catch-ups, family time and time spent outdoors.

THE AUSTRALIAN
Women's Weekly

A whole year
of enjoyment

NOVEMBER						
S	M	T	W	T	F	S
			1	2	3	4
5	6	7	8	9	10	11
12	13	14	15	16	17	18
19	20	21	22	23	24	25
26	27	28	29	30		

DECEMBER						
S	M	T	W	T	F	S
31					1	2
3	4	5	6	7	8	9
10	11	12	13	14	15	16
17	18	19	20	21	22	23
24	25	26	27	28	29	30

JANUARY						
S	M	T	W	T	F	S
	1	2	3	4	5	6
7	8	9	10	11	12	13
14	15	16	17	18	19	20
21	22	23	24	25	26	27
28	29	30	31			

27 MONDAY

28 TUESDAY

29 WEDNESDAY

30 THURSDAY

December
2023

1 FRIDAY

2 SATURDAY

BUY YOUR 2024 DIARY and support breast cancer research. Visit breastcancer trials.org.au, and don't forget this diary makes a great Christmas gift, as well!

3 SUNDAY

NOVEMBER

S	M	T	W	T	F	S
			1	2	3	4
5	6	7	8	9	10	11
12	13	14	15	16	17	18
19	20	21	22	23	24	25
26	27	28	29	30		

DECEMBER

S	M	T	W	T	F	S
31					1	2
3	4	5	6	7	8	9
10	11	12	13	14	15	16
17	18	19	20	21	22	23
24	25	26	27	28	29	30

JANUARY

S	M	T	W	T	F	S
	1	2	3	4	5	6
7	8	9	10	11	12	13
14	15	16	17	18	19	20
21	22	23	24	25	26	27
28	29	30	31			

4 MONDAY

5 TUESDAY

6 WEDNESDAY

7 THURSDAY

December
2023

8 FRIDAY FIRST DAY OF HANUKKAH (JEWISH CELEBRATION)

9 SATURDAY

> **THINKING OF DOWNSIZING?** Living in a smaller home encourages a simpler, more resource-efficient lifestyle, to reduce environmental impact over time.

10 SUNDAY

NOVEMBER

S	M	T	W	T	F	S
			1	2	3	4
5	6	7	8	9	10	11
12	13	14	15	16	17	18
19	20	21	22	23	24	25
26	27	28	29	30		

DECEMBER

S	M	T	W	T	F	S
31					1	2
3	4	5	6	7	8	9
10	11	12	13	14	15	16
17	18	19	20	21	22	23
24	25	26	27	28	29	30

JANUARY

S	M	T	W	T	F	S
	1	2	3	4	5	6
7	8	9	10	11	12	13
14	15	16	17	18	19	20
21	22	23	24	25	26	27
28	29	30	31			

11 MONDAY

12 TUESDAY

13 WEDNESDAY

14 THURSDAY

15 FRIDAY

16 SATURDAY

WHEN SUMMER TEMPERATURES ARE HIGH, stay indoors, drink plenty of fluids like water or herbal tea and check on those at risk of heat stress, including children, the elderly and pets.

17 SUNDAY

NOVEMBER

S	M	T	W	T	F	S
			1	2	3	4
5	6	7	8	9	10	11
12	13	14	15	16	17	18
19	20	21	22	23	24	25
26	27	28	29	30		

DECEMBER

S	M	T	W	T	F	S
31					1	2
3	4	5	6	7	8	9
10	11	12	13	14	15	16
17	18	19	20	21	22	23
24	25	26	27	28	29	30

JANUARY

S	M	T	W	T	F	S
	1	2	3	4	5	6
7	8	9	10	11	12	13
14	15	16	17	18	19	20
21	22	23	24	25	26	27
28	29	30	31			

18 MONDAY

19 TUESDAY

20 WEDNESDAY

21 THURSDAY

December
2023

22 FRIDAY

23 SATURDAY

24 SUNDAY CHRISTMAS EVE

	N O V E M B E R					
S	M	T	W	T	F	S
			1	2	3	4
5	6	7	8	9	10	11
12	13	14	15	16	17	18
19	20	21	22	23	24	25
26	27	28	29	30		

	D E C E M B E R					
S	M	T	W	T	F	S
31					1	2
3	4	5	6	7	8	9
10	11	12	13	14	15	16
17	18	19	20	21	22	23
24	25	26	27	28	29	30

	J A N U A R Y					
S	M	T	W	T	F	S
	1	2	3	4	5	6
7	8	9	10	11	12	13
14	15	16	17	18	19	20
21	22	23	24	25	26	27
28	29	30	31			

25 MONDAY CHRISTMAS DAY

26 TUESDAY BOXING DAY, PROCLAMATION DAY (SA)

27 WEDNESDAY

28 THURSDAY

December
2023

29 FRIDAY

30 SATURDAY

> **HAPPY NEW YEAR!** Jot down some goals or resolutions for the year ahead, and make sure they're realistic and achievable for a greater chance of success.

31 SUNDAY NEW YEAR'S EVE

Notes

Notes

Notes

THE AUSTRALIAN WOMEN'S

Health Diary®

Editor: Tiffany Dunk

Art & Picture Director: Ellen Erickson

Writer & Copy Editor: Stephanie Hope

BCT Diary Manager: Julie Callaghan
Breast Cancer Trials (BCT)
1800 423 444; breastcancertrials.org.au
diaryenquiries@bctrials.org.au

The Australian Women's Health Diary®
is produced by the publishers of
The Australian Women's Weekly on
behalf of Breast Cancer Trials.

THE AUSTRALIAN Women's Weekly

Editor-in-Chief: Nicole Byers

Chief Executive Officer: Jane Huxley

BREAST
CANCER
TRIALS